1540/403

NATIONAL
QUALIFICATIONS
2002

MONDAY, 20 MAY
1.00 PM – 2.45 PM

HISTORY
STANDARD GRADE
Credit Level

Answer questions from Unit I **and** Unit II **and** Unit III.

Choose only **one** Context from each Unit and answer Sections A **and** B. The Contexts chosen should be those you have studied.

The Contexts in each Unit are:

Number the questions as shown in the question paper.

Some sources have been adapted or translated.

SCOTTISH
QUALIFICATIONS
AUTHORITY

UNIT I—CHANGING LIFE IN SCOTLAND AND BRITAIN

CONTEXT A: 1750s–1850s

SECTION A: KNOWLEDGE AND UNDERSTANDING

The life of the ordinary person was subject to many dangers over which he had little or no control.

(Note: for this answer you should write a short essay of several paragraphs.)

1. Explain fully the reasons why people living in nineteenth-century Scotland faced difficulties due to

EITHER

(*a*) problems with housing.   **8**

OR

(*b*) problems with health.   **8**

SECTION B: ENQUIRY SKILLS

The issue for investigating is:

In the early nineteenth century, Scottish textile mills provided acceptable working conditions for the work force.

**Study the sources carefully and answer the questions which follow.
You should use your own knowledge where appropriate.**

Source A is from the Report of Commissioners on the Employment of Children in Factories, 1833.

Source A

The rooms in Deanston Mill (in Stirlingshire) are well ventilated and have the machinery well fenced. The windows are constructed so that the whole of the upper part of each window may be let down. There are rooms for the workers to dress and undress in, and piped water to each storey. Sewering arrangements are adopted throughout.

Source B is from "Expansion, Trade and Industry" by historian C. Culpin, written in 1993.

Source B

> It must have been hard for people used to working on their own at home, at their own speed, to fit into factory work. The powered machines went on, hour after hour, and workers had to keep up with them. Owners of the first factories had strict rules to enforce discipline. Workers had to do as they were told or lose their jobs. There were no safety laws and no protective guards on dangerous machines.

Source C is from an official investigation into working conditions in textile mills in 1833.

Source C

> Large, recently built mills are, without exception, more spacious. The buildings are better drained and more effective methods are used to maintain a moderate temperature. Older, smaller mills have no accommodation for washing or dressing and no machinery for carrying off dust. Some of the rooms are so low that it is scarcely possible to stand upright in the centre of the room.

2. How useful are **Sources A** and **B** for investigating working conditions in Scottish textile mills in the nineteenth century? **4**

3. What evidence is there in the sources to support the view that the Scottish textile industry in the nineteenth century provided good working conditions?

   What evidence in the sources suggests that the Scottish textile industry in the nineteenth century did **not** provide good working conditions? **6**

4. How true is it to say that in the early nineteenth century the Scottish textile mills provided acceptable working conditions for the work force?

   You must use **evidence from the sources** and **your own knowledge** to reach a balanced conclusion. **5**

[END OF CONTEXT IA]

UNIT I—CHANGING LIFE IN SCOTLAND AND BRITAIN

CONTEXT B: 1830s–1930s

SECTION A: KNOWLEDGE AND UNDERSTANDING

> This was a period of significant improvement in the everyday life of the British people.

(Note: for this answer you should write a short essay of several paragraphs.)

1. Explain fully the reasons why people's lives got better between 1830 and 1930 as a result of

EITHER

   (a) improvements in health.   **8**

OR

   (b) improvements in housing.   **8**

SECTION B: ENQUIRY SKILLS

The issue for investigating is:

> By the 1930s working conditions had greatly improved in Scottish coal mines.

Study the sources carefully and answer the questions which follow.
You should use your own knowledge where appropriate.

Source A is from "Britain Transformed" written in 1987 by the historian, Malcolm Falkus.

Source A

> In the later nineteenth century steam driven fans were installed to circulate air in mines. Underground explosions were considerably lessened by the invention of the Davy Safety Lamp. Strong, wire rope became more widely used in all pits. Increasingly, collieries used steam engines for their winding gear. Aspects of safety were also improved by Acts of Parliament.

P
A
D
P
C
A
B
L
E

who
what
where
why
when.

Source B was written in 1869 by David Bremner after his visit to Arniston Colliery in Midlothian.

Source B

> The miners enter the pit between 5 and 6 o'clock in the morning. They are in constant danger of a violent death or of injury. The winding gear may give way and there are the dangers of being suffocated by foul air or of being scorched to death by the ignition of fire damp (methane). In 1865 in Scotland 12 034 638 tons of coal were raised and 77 lives lost.

Source C is from a history textbook and is about working conditions in mines in the 1930s.

Source C

> The dangers of roof falls and cage accidents were still present, though rarer, and fewer lives were lost than in the past. However, new machinery created more dust and more lung disease. Safety clothing was only being introduced in the 1930s. Government legislation resulted in improvements and the miners continued to press for better pay and conditions.

2. How useful are **Sources A** and **B** for investigating improved working conditions in Scottish coal mines in the nineteenth century?   4

3. What evidence is there in the sources that working conditions in Scottish coal mines were improving?

   What evidence in the sources suggests that working conditions in Scottish coal mines had **not** greatly improved?   6

4. To what extent did working conditions greatly improve in Scottish coal mines by the 1930s?

   You must use **evidence from the sources** and **your own knowledge** to reach a balanced conclusion.   5

[END OF CONTEXT IB]

UNIT I—CHANGING LIFE IN SCOTLAND AND BRITAIN

CONTEXT C: 1880s–Present Day

SECTION A: KNOWLEDGE AND UNDERSTANDING

In most parts of Scotland the standards of health and housing greatly improved during the twentieth century.

(Note: for this answer you should write a short essay of several paragraphs.)

1. Explain fully the reasons why people's lives got better in twentieth-century Scotland as a result of

EITHER

(a) improvements in health.   8

OR

(b) improvements in housing.   8

SECTION B: ENQUIRY SKILLS

The issue for investigating is:

Employment opportunities for women were greatly changed by the First World War.

Study the sources carefully and answer the questions which follow.
You should use your own knowledge where appropriate.

Source A is an extract from "The Scottish Nation 1700–2000" by Professor T. M. Devine.

Source A

Male trade unionists strongly supported the idea of "separate spheres" for men and women in which the woman's place was very much in the home. This belief was threatened by the First World War. Women flooded into the munitions factories, engineering workshops and numerous other areas of the economy formerly dominated by men. However, the old ideas about women were very strong and it is no longer possible to speak about the Great War as a turning point in the emancipation of working women.

Source B was published in the Glasgow Evening Citizen newspaper in April, 1916.

Source B

> When the history of the war is written, the part played by women will be one of its finest chapters. From every class they have come forward to help their country: as nurses, as workers and in the thousand and one occupations in town and country that were previously filled by men.

Source C is from "The Cause" by E. R. Strachey, written in 1928.

Source C

> After the war, thousands of women workers were dismissed and could find no work to do. It was terribly hard on women. Everyone assumed they would go quietly back to their homes but this was impossible. War deaths had enormously increased the number of surplus women so that one in three had to be self-supporting. The tone of the press changed and the very same women who had been heroines were now parasites.

2. How useful are **Sources A** and **B** for investigating the effects of the First World War on women's employment opportunities?   4

3. What evidence is there in the sources to support the view that the First World War greatly changed employment opportunities for women?

   What evidence is there in the sources to support the view that the First World War did **not** greatly change employment opportunities for women?   6

4. To what extent did the First World War greatly change employment opportunities for women?

   You must use **evidence from the sources** and **your own knowledge** to reach a balanced conclusion.   5

[END OF CONTEXT IC]

UNIT II—INTERNATIONAL COOPERATION AND CONFLICT

CONTEXT A: 1790s–1820s

SECTION A: KNOWLEDGE AND UNDERSTANDING

> As the French Revolution daily grew more violent, so the danger of war increased.

1. How important was the fear of revolution in causing the war between Britain and France?   **4**

> There was considerable discontent in the navy and this was to show itself in the mutinies of 1797.

2. Describe the hardships faced by sailors in the navy during the Wars with France.   **5**

SECTION B: ENQUIRY SKILLS

The following sources are about the Congress of Vienna in 1815.

Study the sources carefully and answer the questions which follow.
You should use your own knowledge where appropriate.

Source A is from the writings of the nineteenth-century Italian politician, Cavour.

Source A

> The Congress of Vienna built a Europe without moral or just foundations. It relied upon no principle, neither rights of legal rulers, nor national interests, nor the will of the people. It took no account of geographical conditions or of general interests and acted only by right of the strongest.

3. Discuss the attitude of Cavour to the settlement reached at the Congress of Vienna.   **4**

In **Source B**, the historians D. Richards and J. W. Hunt give their view of the Congress of Vienna.

Source B

> The treaties completely ignored the spirit of nationality which had proved so powerful in defeating Napoleon. Countries and peoples were moved about regardless of their wishes and feelings. But, however great its faults, the settlement showed some wisdom. The chief British representative, Lord Castlereagh, determined that France should not be victimised for the faults of Napoleon.

4.   To what extent do the authors of **Source B** agree with Cavour in **Source A**?   5

[END OF CONTEXT IIA]

UNIT II—INTERNATIONAL COOPERATION AND CONFLICT

> ### CONTEXT B: 1890s–1920s

SECTION A: KNOWLEDGE AND UNDERSTANDING

> By 1914 Britain and Germany stared menacingly at each other across the North Sea.

1. How important a factor was naval rivalry in causing tension before 1914?   **4**

> By early 1916 trench lines were well established on the Western Front.

2. Describe what trench life was like for front line soldiers on the Western Front.   **5**

SECTION B: ENQUIRY SKILLS

The following sources are about the Treaty of Versailles.

**Study the sources carefully and answer the questions which follow.
You should use your own knowledge where appropriate.**

Source A was written by Sir Philip Gibbs who was a British representative at the peace conference.

Source A

> 'It was a peace of vengeance and consequently was very unfair. The economic terms of the Treaty were mad. Germany had to pay for all the damage caused during the war. The impossibility of getting all this money from a defeated country was obvious even to the most ignorant schoolboy.

3. Discuss the attitude of Sir Philip Gibbs towards the Treaty of Versailles.   **4**

Source B is part of a speech by Lloyd George in July 1919.

Source B

> The last time I spoke about the Treaty I called it a "stern but just treaty". I stick to that description. The terms are in many respects terrible terms to impose upon a country. Germany's war debt is more than doubled in order to pay reparations. However, in so far as territories have been taken away from Germany, it is a restoration—they are all territories that ought not to belong to Germany.

4. How far do **Sources A** and **B** disagree about the Treaty of Versailles?　　　5

[END OF CONTEXT IIB]

UNIT II—INTERNATIONAL COOPERATION AND CONFLICT

CONTEXT C: 1930s–1960s

SECTION A: KNOWLEDGE AND UNDERSTANDING

> Hitler had his eye on Czechoslovakia, especially the Sudetenland.

1. How important was the Czech crisis of 1938 as a cause of increasing tension before the Second World War?

4

> Government wartime controls affected almost every aspect of life in Britain.

2. Describe the hardships of everyday life for civilians in Britain during the Second World War.

5

SECTION B: ENQUIRY SKILLS

The following sources are about the changing role of Britain and its Empire.

**Study the sources carefully and answer the questions which follow.
You should use your own knowledge where appropriate.**

Source A is from the autobiography of Clement Attlee, British Prime Minister from 1945–1951.

Source A

> Our policy was to give full self-government to our former colonies. Britain is now the heart of a growing Commonwealth. This policy met with general approval except from a limited number of people, including Churchill, who regarded it as a betrayal of our imperial heritage. In fact, we have gained immensely in friendship from our policy. An attempt to maintain old colonialism would have aided communism.

3. Discuss the attitude of Clement Attlee about Britain's changing policy towards its former colonies.

4

In **Source B** a modern historian discusses Britain's changing influence after 1945.

Source B

> In 1945 the British people still thought of their country as a great imperial power but the British were breaking up their once world-wide Empire. In a few places there was fighting but more often power was handed over peacefully. Only a few regretted this, believing that the Empire had made Britain great. Britain tried to keep on friendly terms with its old colonies through the Commonwealth, the group of independent nations who had once been part of the British Empire.

4. To what extent do **Sources A** and **B** agree about Britain's changing influence after 1945?

5

[END OF CONTEXT IIC]

UNIT III—PEOPLE AND POWER

CONTEXT A: USA 1850–1880

SECTION A: KNOWLEDGE AND UNDERSTANDING

> When war broke out in 1861 many Northerners were firmly against slavery.

1. Explain the reasons why many people in the North were against slavery.   **3**

> After the Civil War was over the government improved the position of the freed slaves.

2. In what ways did the US government improve the conditions of the freed slaves after 1865?   **4**

SECTION B: ENQUIRY SKILLS

The following sources are about Westward expansion.

Study the sources carefully and answer the questions which follow.
You should use your own knowledge where appropriate.

Source A was painted by Francis Palmer in 1866. It is called "Rocky Mountains— Emigrants Crossing the Plains".

Source A

3. How useful is **Source A** as evidence of how white settlers travelled west?   **4**

In **Source B** a native American ("Indian") discusses the white settlers' attitude to land ownership.

Source B

> Why do these "People Greedily Grasping for Land" want more acres than they need to grow food on? Why do they build houses that will outlast their occupants? Why does the white man insist that land he has bought becomes his exclusively and for all time? Sell a country? Why not sell the air, the clouds and the great sea?

4. Discuss the attitude of the native American ("Indian") towards land ownership shown in **Source B**.

4

Source C is from "The American West, 1840–1895" by R. A. Rees and S. J. Styles.

Source C

> White American Settlers believed that they were not simply looking for new and fertile farmland, they were putting the American dream into action. They were beginning the final wave of migration which would end with the whole of America being lived in by white Americans. They believed that civilisation would be brought to the wilderness.

5. How fully does the evidence given in **Source C** explain the reasons for settlers going west?

   You must use **evidence from the source** and **your own knowledge** and give reasons for your answer.

4

[END OF CONTEXT IIIA]

UNIT III—PEOPLE AND POWER

CONTEXT B: INDIA 1917–1947

SECTION A: KNOWLEDGE AND UNDERSTANDING

> Lord Curzon, Viceroy of India, sincerely believed in British superiority in all things.

1. Explain in what ways many Indians were increasingly discontented with British rule after 1917.

3

> Gandhi's tactics have had far reaching consequences outside India.

2. Describe Gandhi's tactics in resisting British power.

4

SECTION B: ENQUIRY SKILLS

The following sources are about Indian Independence and Partition.

**Study the sources carefully and answer the questions which follow.
You should use your own knowledge where appropriate.**

Source A is a press photograph which appeared in British newspapers on August 16th, 1947.

Source A

NEW DELHI: INDEPENDENCE DAY
HAPPY CROWDS MOB LORD AND LADY MOUNTBATTEN

3. How useful is **Source A** as evidence of attitudes in India towards Independence?   **4**

Source B is from a speech given by Winston Churchill in September 1947.

Source B

> The fearful massacres which are occurring in India are no surprise to me. This is just the beginning of the horrors and butcheries which will be carried out. The peoples of India are gifted with the capacities for the highest culture and they had for generations dwelt side by side in general peace under the tolerant and impartial rule of the British Crown and Parliament. Now things will be different.

4. Discuss Winston Churchill's views about the difficulties following India's Independence.   **4**

Source C is from "The Long Afternoon" by William Golant.

Source C

> In the past, the two separate communities had lived uneasily together. Even under British rule the two religions had separate education and languages which contributed to an aggressive attitude toward each other's community. In some areas such as Bengal and the Punjab the majority of the population were Muslims.

5. How fully does **Source C** explain the difficulties faced by an independent India?

    You must use **evidence from the source** and **your own knowledge** and give reasons for your answer.   **4**

[END OF CONTEXT IIIB]

UNIT III—PEOPLE AND POWER

CONTEXT C: RUSSIA 1914–1941

SECTION A: KNOWLEDGE AND UNDERSTANDING

> "There was evidence of widespread discontent with the Tsar's government by the end of 1916."

1. Why were so many Russians discontented with the Tsar's government by late 1916?   **3**

> Lenin was convinced that the time was right to take power from the Provisional Government.

2. Describe the seizure of power by the Bolsheviks in October 1917.   **4**

SECTION B: ENQUIRY SKILLS

The following sources are about the Provisional Government.

**Study the sources carefully and answer the questions which follow.
You should use your own knowledge where appropriate.**

Source A is from a speech by Lenin in April 1917.

Source A

> Do not believe the promises of the Provisional Government. They are deceiving you and the whole Russian people. The people need peace; the people need bread; the people need land. And they give you war, hunger, no bread and leave the landlords still on the land. We must fight for the social revolution.

3. Discuss Lenin's views about the Provisional Government.   **4**

Source B is a photograph from 1917 showing wounded soldiers demonstrating. The banner says "Continue the War until Victory is Complete".

Source B

4. How useful is **Source B** as evidence about attitudes in Russia towards the Provisional Government?

4

Source C is from "Lenin and the Russian Revolution" by Donald W. Mack.

Source C

> The Provisional Government was unable to improve matters, and the workers began to try to get control of the factories in which they worked. Some argued that Russia should be governed by the Soviets. This was what the Bolsheviks were saying so they found allies in the workers who were prepared to overthrow the Provisional Government.

5. How fully does **Source C** explain why the Provisional Government fell from power in October, 1917?

You must use **evidence from the source** and **your own knowledge** and give reasons for your answer.

4

[*END OF CONTEXT IIIC*]

UNIT III—PEOPLE AND POWER

CONTEXT D: GERMANY 1918–1939

SECTION A: KNOWLEDGE AND UNDERSTANDING

> The Weimar Government in Germany was unpopular in the years following the Versailles Settlement.

1. Explain why the Weimar Government was unpopular with many Germans in the early 1920s.　　3

> By 1934 Hitler was the Fuhrer with complete control over the German people.

2. Describe the ways in which Hitler gained total power in Germany.　　4

SECTION B: ENQUIRY SKILLS

The following sources are about attitudes to the Nazis.

**Study the sources carefully and answer the questions which follow.
You should use your own knowledge where appropriate.**

Source A is an extract from the diary of Count Harry Kessler written after an election in 1932.

Source A

> A black day for Germany. The Nazis have increased their number of seats almost tenfold. They have become the second largest party in the Reichstag. The impression created abroad must be disastrous. The impact on foreign and financial affairs is likely to be very damaging. We face a national crisis. This can only be overcome if all those who accept or at least tolerate the Republic stand firmly together.

3. Discuss the attitude of Count Kessler towards the Nazis.　　4

Source B is a Nazi poster from 1933. The German words say "Our last hope: HITLER".

Source B

4. How useful is **Source B** as evidence of the tactics used by the Nazis to gain support?   **4**

In **Source C** a modern historian describes the problems faced by Germans who opposed the Nazis.

Source C

> The resistance movement never enjoyed much support among the masses of the working class. It was a movement of officers without soldiers: a large and uncoordinated collection of intellectuals, civil servants, diplomats and the military. Each group was rarely informed about what the other groups were doing.

5. How fully does the evidence in **Source C** explain why it was difficult to oppose the Nazis?

   You must use **evidence from the source** and **your own knowledge** and give reasons for your answer.   **4**

[END OF CONTEXT IIID]

[END OF QUESTION PAPER]

[BLANK PAGE]

[BLANK PAGE]

[BLANK PAGE]

G

1540/402

NATIONAL
QUALIFICATIONS
2002

MONDAY, 20 MAY
10.20 AM – 11.50 AM

HISTORY
STANDARD GRADE
General Level

Answer questions from Unit I **and** Unit II **and** Unit III.

Choose only **one** Context from each Unit and answer Sections A **and** B. The Contexts chosen should be those you have studied.

The Contexts in each Unit are:

You must use the information in the sources, and your own knowledge, to answer the questions.

Number the questions as shown in the question paper.

Some sources have been adapted or translated.

SCOTTISH
QUALIFICATIONS
AUTHORITY
©

UNIT I—CHANGING LIFE IN SCOTLAND AND BRITAIN

> ### CONTEXT A: 1750s–1850s

SECTION A: KNOWLEDGE AND UNDERSTANDING

Study the information in the sources. You must also use your own knowledge in your answers.

In **Source A** the historian Simon Mason writes about changes to the population of Britain in the eighteenth century.

Source A

> The death rate fell steeply after 1770 and continued to fall. After 1790 there were still years of bad harvests but nothing approaching a famine. There were plenty of diseases but no epidemics. There was also a definite rise in the standard of living in the eighteenth century.

1. Why did the population of Britain rise in the eighteenth century?　　　　4

Source B gives evidence of the changes made in Scotland by the Reform Act of 1832.

Source B

> The Act, though a moderate measure, corrected the worst abuses of the old system. The new voters were shopkeepers and skilled workers in the burghs and wealthy farmers in the counties. If the Radicals still complained that most workers remained voteless, more political power to the middle class was a real advance.

2. Describe the changes brought about by the Reform Act of 1832.　　　　3

SECTION B: ENQUIRY SKILLS

The issue for investigating is:

> Changes in agriculture between 1750 and 1850 were good for Scotland.

Study the sources carefully and answer the questions which follow.

You should use your own knowledge where appropriate.

Source C was written in a report by Sir John Sinclair, MP in 1814.

Source C

> The great advantage to Scotland of threshing mills being now so common, is that the amount of manual labour is greatly reduced. Also the quantity of agricultural produce is greatly increased. Managing farming on large estates has become much easier.

3. How useful is **Source C** for investigating the effects of changes in agriculture in Scotland after 1750?

3

Source D is from "Changing Life in Scotland and Britain" by Craig Madden.

Source D

> Many poorer tenants lost their land and became farm labourers. Many such labourers were later put out of work by the introduction of farm machines and were reduced to begging. Others left the countryside altogether, and found jobs in towns. The tragedy of the disappearance of the small tenant farmer can be seen in the number of deserted villages.

4. What evidence in **Source C** agrees with the view that changes in agriculture were good for Scotland?

   What evidence in **Source D** does **not** agree with the view that changes in agriculture were good for Scotland?

5

5. How far do you agree that changes in agriculture between 1750 and 1850 were good for Scotland?

   You must use evidence **from the sources** and **your own knowledge** to come to a conclusion.

4

[END OF CONTEXT IA]

Now turn to the Context you have chosen in Unit II.

UNIT I—CHANGING LIFE IN SCOTLAND AND BRITAIN

CONTEXT B: 1830s–1930s

SECTION A: KNOWLEDGE AND UNDERSTANDING

Study the information in the sources. You must also use your own knowledge in your answers.

In **Source A** the historian Malcolm Falkus discusses population growth in Britain in the period 1830–1880.

Source A

> Earlier historians laid great importance for population growth on medical treatment. Now emphasis is on social factors such as better diet, less overcrowding and greater cleanliness. Less credit is given to the medical profession.

1. Why did the population of Britain grow between 1830 and 1880?   4

In **Source B** the historian Alastair Gray describes changes in voting in Scotland.

Source B

> In 1868 a Second Reform Act gave skilled workmen the vote and so 230 000 men in Scotland could take part in elections. In 1884, a Third Reform Act was passed. This meant that farm workers, crofters, miners and other working men could now vote.

2. Describe the changes in voting between 1850 and 1930.   3

SECTION B: ENQUIRY SKILLS

The issue for investigating is:

> The development of railways between 1850 and 1930 was good for Scotland.

Study the sources carefully and answer the questions which follow.

You should use your own knowledge where appropriate.

Source C was written in "The Railway Magazine" in January 1921.

Source C

> Express trains from Edinburgh and Glasgow make Aberdeen station busy with travellers. During the Glasgow Holiday week of 1920, 15 000 people travelled to Aberdeen. Trains also carry 60 000 tons of fish to English markets. Horses and pedigree cattle are moved by rail from the North East to other parts of the country.

3. How useful is **Source C** for investigating how railways were used in Scotland between 1850 and 1930?   3

Source D is from "The Scottish Railway Story", published in 1992.

Source D

> There were those who objected to some of the changes which the railway brought in its wake, such as Sunday travel or the pollution of the town or countryside. Sections of the community saw the coming of the railways as a threat, the coach owners understandably.

4. What evidence is there in **Source C** that the development of railways was good for Scotland?

    What evidence is there in **Source D** that the development of railways was **not** good for Scotland?   5

5. How far do you agree that the development of railways between 1850 and 1930 was good for Scotland?

    You must use evidence **from the sources** and **your own knowledge** to come to a conclusion.   4

[END OF CONTEXT IB]

Now turn to the Context you have chosen in Unit II.

UNIT I—CHANGING LIFE IN SCOTLAND AND BRITAIN

CONTEXT C: 1880s–Present Day

SECTION A: KNOWLEDGE AND UNDERSTANDING

Study the information in the sources. You must also use your own knowledge in your answers.

In **Source A** the historian John Patrick writes about population changes in Britain after 1880.

Source A

> Medical improvements helped to reduce the death rate. Better housing meant there was less chance of disease spreading. People were also living longer because of a healthier diet. At the same time, however, the birth rate had fallen so old people made up a much greater proportion of the population than ever before.

1. Why did the population of Britain continue to grow after 1880? **4**

Source B was said by Lord Birkenhead in 1928.

Source B

> In 1918 I was against the extension of the franchise to women of any age. I am now against the giving of the vote to women over 21 years of age. This all began in 1918 when a Member of Parliament said, "If you are giving the vote to our brave soldiers how about our brave female munition workers as well?"

2. Describe changes in voting between 1900 and 1969. **3**

SECTION B: ENQUIRY SKILLS

The issue for investigating is:

> Developments in road transport in the twentieth century were good for Scotland.

Study the sources carefully and answer the questions which follow.

You should use your own knowledge where appropriate.

In **Source C** a Glasgow resident remembers when the M8 motorway was built in the 1960s.

Source C

> There were streets here, with tenements built at the start of the century. They were very solid houses with good sized bedrooms. Well, a slum order was put on them and we were forced out in 1965 and rehoused in new flats. There was nothing wrong with our old place. The council were just desperate to pull it down for the new, noisy motorway coming through.

3. How useful is **Source C** for investigating the effects of developments in road transport in Scotland? **3**

Source D is from a modern history book.

Source D

> Petrol vehicles have brought a great deal of fun and freedom into many people's lives. They have helped bring cheaper goods into the shops. Thousands of Scots make their living from the transport industries. Communities that were once isolated are now within a few hours' reach of Glasgow and Edinburgh.

4. What evidence in **Source C** does **not** agree with the view that developments in road transport were good for Scotland?

   What evidence in **Source D** agrees with the view that developments in road transport were good for Scotland? **5**

5. How far do you agree that developments in road transport were good for Scotland?

   You must use evidence **from the sources** and **your own knowledge** to come to a conclusion. **4**

[END OF CONTEXT IC]

Now turn to the Context you have chosen in Unit II.

UNIT II—INTERNATIONAL COOPERATION AND CONFLICT

CONTEXT A: 1790s–1820s

SECTION A: KNOWLEDGE AND UNDERSTANDING

Study the information in the sources. You must also use your own knowledge in your answers.

Source A is about the causes of the Revolutionary War.

Source A

> The execution of King Louis XVI appeared to many people in Britain as a barbaric and unjustified act which made the Revolution the enemy of all kings. Prime Minister Pitt protested to the French ambassador in London, and the French reply was a declaration of war.

1. Explain why Britain went to war against France in 1793. **4**

Source B describes an effect of the war on civilians in Britain.

Source B

> The Wars brought misery upon the working classes because of a great rise in the cost of living. Bread in particular rose in price because imports of wheat were difficult to obtain. The price of wheat almost tripled from 1790 to 1812.

2. How serious were problems of food supply for the British people during the wars with France? **3**

SECTION B: ENQUIRY SKILLS

The following sources are about the Fourth Coalition against France, 1813–1814.

Study the sources carefully and answer the questions which follow.

You should use your own knowledge where appropriate.

Source C is a cartoon by the British Artist, James Gilray, published in 1814. It shows Napoleon being attacked on all sides.

Source C

3. How useful is **Source C** as evidence about the Fourth Coalition against France?   4

In **Source D** the historian H. L. Peacock describes one success of the Fourth Coalition.

Source D

> At Leipzig, the "Battle of the Nations" involving 500 000 men was fought on October 16th–18th, 1813. The allies included Austrians, Prussians, Russians and Swedes. Napoleon, attacked on all sides, was defeated and flung back over the Rhine.

4. How far do **Sources C** and **D** agree about the Fourth Coalition against France?   4

5. How fully does **Source D** explain why the Fourth Coalition against France was successful?

    You should use **your own knowledge** and give reasons for your answer.   4

[END OF CONTEXT IIA]

Now turn to the Context you have chosen in Unit III.

UNIT II—INTERNATIONAL COOPERATION AND CONFLICT

CONTEXT B: 1890s–1920s

SECTION A: KNOWLEDGE AND UNDERSTANDING

Study the information in the sources. You must also use your own knowledge in your answers.

Source A is from a modern history textbook by Tony Howarth.

Source A

> On 28 June 1914 the heir to the Austrian throne, Archduke Franz Ferdinand and his wife were shot dead in Sarajevo, the capital of Bosnia. The assassin, Gavrilo Princip, was a Bosnian Serb who wanted Bosnian independence from Austria. But Austria blamed Serbia and used the murders as an excuse to smash Serbian nationalism.

1. Explain why the assassinations at Sarajevo led to the outbreak of the First World War. **4**

Source B is from the war memoirs of British Prime Minister, Lloyd George.

Source B

> The steady improvement in our national health figures during and after the war shows that food rationing did more good than harm. Although there was some scarcity, we were never faced with famine or actual hardship.

2. How serious a problem was rationing for British civilians during the First World War? **3**

SECTION B: ENQUIRY SKILLS

The following sources are about tanks in the First World War.

Study the sources carefully and answer the questions which follow.

You should use your own knowledge where appropriate.

Source C is a photograph from the Imperial War Museum collection of a tank in action in 1916.

Source C

3. How useful is **Source C** as evidence of the use of tanks in the First World War?   **4**

Source D is from a modern history textbook.

Source D

> The tank had a maximum speed—on a good road—of about six kilometres an hour. It was driven by caterpillar tracks, protected by steel armour and could carry four machine guns. They were to be used against entanglements of barbed wire. Tanks had a crew of eight who had to face many problems.

4. How far do **Sources C** and **D** agree about the tank?   **4**

Source E was written in the memoirs of Lieutenant F. Mitchell who was in charge of a tank in 1917.

Source E

> The tank that went for the pill box got stuck in the mud. As it sank deeper, it fired desperately. By chance, its six-pounder gun pointed straight inside the pill box door and most of the German garrison of 60 men was killed by the tank's fire. There were only 29 British casualties instead of a thousand. The tank had shown its qualities.

5. How fully does **Source E** describe the use of tanks in the First World War?

    You should use **your own knowledge** and give reasons for your answer.   **4**

[END OF CONTEXT IIB]

Now turn to the Context you have chosen in Unit III.

UNIT II—INTERNATIONAL COOPERATION AND CONFLICT

CONTEXT C: 1930s–1960s

SECTION A: KNOWLEDGE AND UNDERSTANDING

Study the information in the sources. You must also use your own knowledge in your answers.

Source A describes why Hitler attacked Poland in 1939.

Source A

> Hitler wanted Danzig. The people of Danzig were mainly German. They had been separated from Germany by the "Polish Corridor" in 1919. The Poles refused to give in to Hitler's demands. Soon Hitler was demanding the whole of Western Poland.

1. Explain why Germany attacked Poland in September 1939.   **4**

Source B explains the building of the Berlin Wall.

Source B

> When he met John Kennedy in 1961 Khrushchev thought he could dominate him and insisted that America recognise the existence of East Germany. Kennedy refused and America prepared for war. In revenge, the Soviets built a wall right across Berlin.

2. How important was the Berlin crisis of 1961 as a threat to world peace?   **3**

SECTION B: ENQUIRY SKILLS

The following sources are about air raids during the Second World War.

Study the sources carefully and answer the questions which follow.

You should use your own knowledge where appropriate.

Source C is a description of a bombing raid on Clydeside from the Glasgow Herald, 15 May 1941.

Source C

> Houses, churches and schools in the area were wrecked. In this district hardly a pane of glass remained in shop windows. Streets were strewn with broken glass, rubble and debris. People spent yesterday recovering property and furniture from their partially ruined homes and shops.

3. How useful is **Source C** as evidence of the effects of an air raid in the Second World War?   **4**

Source D shows the aftermath of an air raid on Menzies Road, Aberdeen on August 8th, 1941.

Source D

4. To what extent do **Sources C** and **D** agree about the effects of an air raid?   **4**

In **Source E** a young Scotswoman describes an air raid in 1941.

Source E

> We heard the wail of the sirens and in the silence after that we could hear the drone of a plane. There was panic as instinct drove us all towards the door and the stairs. Women and girls were white faced and shaking. Then the bombs fell.

5. How fully does the evidence in **Source E** explain what happened in an air raid?

   You should use **your own knowledge** and give reasons for your answer.   **4**

[END OF CONTEXT IIC]

Now turn to the Context you have chosen in Unit III.

UNIT III—PEOPLE AND POWER

CONTEXT A: USA 1850–1880

SECTION A: KNOWLEDGE AND UNDERSTANDING

Study the information in the sources. You must also use your own knowledge in your answers.

Source A gives evidence about the effects of railroad building on the west.

Source A

> Thousands of farms were created close to the rail routes. On the Great Plains, the railroads gave a great boost to homesteading farmers. Ranching and the cattle industry also benefited from the railroads as animals could be transported easily. Some cities grew large because of the railroads.

1. Describe the effects of the railroads on the west of America.   3

Source B was printed in a Southern newspaper in 1860.

Source B

> Northerners have robbed us of our property. They have murdered our citizens while they were trying to get our property back. They have ignored the laws of the Supreme Court and now have capped it all by electing Abraham Lincoln as President.

2. Explain why many Southerners were angry with Northerners in 1860.   3

SECTION B: ENQUIRY SKILLS

The following sources are about relationships between native Americans (Indians) and the US Government.

Study the sources carefully and answer the questions which follow.

You should use your own knowledge where appropriate.

Source C is from a speech given by Red Cloud, a Sioux Chief, to a representative of the US Government in 1866.

Source C

> You are the White Chief who has come to steal the road (the Bozeman Trail). The Great Father (US President) sends us presents and wants us to sell him the road but the White Chief comes with soldiers to steal it before our people say "yes" or "no". I will talk with you no more. I will go now and fight you. As long as I live, I will fight for the last hunting grounds of my people.

3. What is the attitude of Red Cloud towards the American Government?   **3**

Source D is taken from "Native Peoples of North America" by Susan Edmonds.

Source D

> The Sioux, fearing a white invasion and the destruction of the buffalo herds, began attacking soldiers on the Bozeman Trail. In 1866 Red Cloud received news that the US Government was planning to build forts along the Trail. After much fighting between the US Army and the Sioux, the government made peace with Red Cloud.

4. How far do **Sources C** and **D** agree about Sioux attitudes to the Bozeman Trail?   **3**

[END OF CONTEXT IIIA]

UNIT III—PEOPLE AND POWER

CONTEXT B: INDIA 1917–1947

SECTION A: KNOWLEDGE AND UNDERSTANDING

Study the information in the sources. You must also use your own knowledge in your answers.

In **Source A** a modern historian writes about the Untouchables.

Source A

> The outcasts in Indian society were called Untouchables and they had to do the tasks which other Hindus would not do. They were below the caste system: creatures whose very shadows could contaminate.

1. Explain why life was unpleasant for the Untouchables.   **3**

Source B is from "The Life of Mahatma Gandhi" by Louis Fischer

Source B

> Some Hindus never forgave Gandhi for his love of Untouchables. But to vast multitudes he was the Mahatma. They asked his blessing; they were happy to touch his feet; they kissed the ground where he passed.

2. Describe the different views of Gandhi held by Indians.   **3**

SECTION B: ENQUIRY SKILLS

The following sources are about the events at Amritsar in 1919.

Study the sources carefully and answer the questions which follow.

You should use your own knowledge where appropriate.

Source C is from the Hunter Report into the events at Amritsar on April 13th, 1919.

Source C

> As soon as General Dyer arrived he entered with his troops. Without giving the crowd any warning he ordered his troops to fire. The firing continued for about ten minutes. There is no evidence of the kind of speech the audience was listening to. None of them had any firearms. The soldiers fired 1650 rounds of ammunition. The crowd was a perfect target.

3. What did the author of the Hunter Report think about the actions of General Dyer? **3**

Source D was written by the historian J. Simkin.

Source D

> General Dyer sent town criers round Amritsar to inform the people that all public meetings were banned. It was later discovered that his orders were not read in places where most people would hear them. When Dyer heard about a meeting he took ninety soldiers and immediately gave instructions for them to fire into the defenceless crowd until they ran out of ammunition. No warning was given and when the riflemen had finished, 379 Indians lay dead.

4. In what ways do **Sources C** and **D** agree about events at Amritsar? **3**

[END OF CONTEXT IIIB]

UNIT III—PEOPLE AND POWER

CONTEXT C: RUSSIA 1914–1941

SECTION A: KNOWLEDGE AND UNDERSTANDING

Study the information in the sources. You must also use your own knowledge in your answers.

In **Source A**, a modern historian describes events in February, 1917.

Source A

> Demonstrations broke out in Petrograd. Women protesting about food shortages were supported by striking factory workers. To make matters worse, troops sent to stop the disturbances mutinied.

1. Describe the main events of the February Revolution. **3**

In **Source B** a kulak explains his opposition to Stalin's collectivisation policy.

Source B

> Whoever heard of such a thing—to give up our land and our animals; to hand over our tools and our farm buildings; to work all the time and divide everything with others?

2. Why did the kulaks oppose Stalin's plans to collectivise Russian agriculture? **3**

SECTION B: ENQUIRY SKILLS

The following sources are about the situation in Russia at the start of the Civil War in 1918.

Study the sources carefully and answer the questions which follow.

You should use your own knowledge where appropriate.

In **Source C** Bukharin, a member of the Bolshevik Government, describes their White opponents.

Source C

> There can be no question of freedom for our opponents. The Bolshevik Party does not allow freedom of the press or freedom of speech for them. They are the enemies of the people. The Party must ruthlessly put down all attempts by our White opponents to return to power. We alone maintain order.

3. What did Bukharin think of opponents of the Bolshevik Party?   **3**

Source D is from a speech by Kaledin, leader of the Don Cossacks, in early 1918.

Source D

> The Cossacks consider the acts of the Bolsheviks to be criminal and ruthless. Until the return of the Provisional Government to power and the restoration of law and order in Russia, I have taken on myself all power in the Don region.

4. How far do **Sources C** and **D** agree about the Bolsheviks and their actions?   **3**

[END OF CONTEXT IIIC]

UNIT III—PEOPLE AND POWER

CONTEXT D: GERMANY 1918–1939

SECTION A: KNOWLEDGE AND UNDERSTANDING

Study the information in the sources. You must also use your own knowledge in your answers.

Source A is from a report by the Mayor of Berlin in 1923.

Source A

> Many children, even the youngest, never get a drop of milk and come to school without a warm breakfast. The children frequently have no shirt or warm clothing. Terrible poverty gradually weakens any sense of cleanliness and leaves room only for thoughts of the struggle against hunger and cold.

1. Describe some of the problems faced by Germans during the period of hyperinflation in 1923.

   3

Source B is about the support Hitler enjoyed during the 1930s.

Source B

> Hitler was popular because he was successful. He gave a strong lead after years of weak government and social conflict. Through the use of rallies and ceremonial events the Nazis kept up an image of confidence and purpose.

2. Why was Hitler so popular with many Germans in the 1930s?

   3

SECTION B: ENQUIRY SKILLS

The following sources are about Hitler's attitude to the Jews.

Study the sources carefully and answer the questions which follow.

You should use your own knowledge where appropriate.

Source C is from a speech made by Hitler in 1922.

Source C

> The Jews are a people of robbers. They have never founded civilisation, though they have destroyed civilisations by the hundred. They have created nothing of their own. They have no art of their own but bit by bit they have stolen it from other people. They have watched them at work and then made their copies.

3. What was Hitler's attitude towards the Jews?   3

In **Source D** a modern historian describes Hitler's attitude towards the Jews.

Source D

> Hitler believed that Aryan superiority was being threatened by the Jewish race. He argued that they were lazy and had contributed little to world civilisation. According to Hitler, Jews were responsible for everything he did not like, including modern art. He also claimed that Jews had been responsible for Germany losing the First World War.

4. How far do **Sources C** and **D** agree about Hitler's attitude to the Jews?   3

[END OF CONTEXT IIID]

[END OF QUESTION PAPER]

[BLANK PAGE]

[BLANK PAGE]

[BLANK PAGE]

OFFICIAL SQA PAST PAPERS WITH SQA ANSWER TIPS

Standard Grade General and Credit
HISTORY
1999 to 2001 with two years' answers

First exam paper published in 1999.

Published by
Leckie & Leckie Ltd, 8 Whitehill Terrace, St. Andrews, Scotland KY16 8RN
tel: 01334 475656 fax: 01334 477392
hq@leckieandleckie.co.uk www.leckieandleckie.co.uk

Leckie & Leckie Project Management Team: Tom Davie; David Nicoll; Bruce Ryan, Andrea Smith
Cover Design Assistance: Mike Middleton

ISBN 1-84372-007-8

A CIP Catalogue record for this book is available from the British Library.

Printed in Scotland by Inglis Allen on environmentally friendly paper. The paper is made from a mixture of sawmill waste, forest thinnings and wood from sustainable forests.

® Leckie & Leckie is a registered trademark.

INVESTOR IN PEOPLE Leckie & Leckie Ltd achieved the Investors in People Standard in 1999.

Leckie & Leckie

Introduction

The best way to prepare for exams is to practise, again and again, all that you have learned over the past year. Attempt these questions and check your solutions against these *Official SQA Answers*. But give yourself a real chance and be honest! Doing this will help you gain not only a proper understanding of each topic but also the maximum marks possible from the examiners! Developing this working habit now will make it easier to do this in the exam!

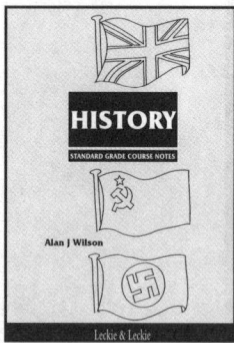

Leckie & Leckie's Standard Grade History Course Notes.
Brilliant, fascinating notes of change and developments from 1750 to the present day. Regular use of this book through the course will ensure the final exam is consigned to your past.

Contents

Leckie & Leckie has made every effort to trace all copyright holders. If any have been inadvertently overlooked, Leckie & Leckie will be pleased to make the necessary arrangements. Leckie & Leckie would like to thank the following for their permission to reproduce their material:

Pearson Education for an extract from *Abraham Lincoln* by Norman Kolpas (p 88).

G

1540/102

| SCOTTISH CERTIFICATE OF EDUCATION 1999 | THURSDAY, 13 MAY
G/C 9.00 AM – 10.30 AM
F/G 10.20 AM – 11.50 AM | **HISTORY STANDARD GRADE** General Level |

Answer questions from Unit I **and** Unit II **and** Unit III.

Choose only **one** Context from each Unit and answer Sections A **and** B. The Contexts chosen should be those you have studied.

The Contexts in each Unit are:

You must use the information in the sources, and your own knowledge, to answer the questions.

Number the questions as shown in the question paper.

Some sources have been adapted or translated.

SCOTTISH QUALIFICATIONS AUTHORITY

UNIT I—CHANGING LIFE IN SCOTLAND AND BRITAIN

CONTEXT A: 1750s–1850s

SECTION A: KNOWLEDGE AND UNDERSTANDING

Study the information in the sources. You must also use your own knowledge in your answers.

Source A is from a letter about changes in farming, written in 1776.

Source A

> Lord Kames described the new chain plough to his tenants. He also got them to enclose their farms and to remove every stone on their land.

1. Describe some of the changes in farming between the 1750s and 1850s.   **4**

Source B is part of a description of changes to farm housing.

Source B

> Farm buildings were greatly improved. Houses were rebuilt with whitewashed stone walls, slate roofs and glass windows. However, some housing in rural areas was still poor. Many farm workers still lived in bad conditions despite the growing wealth of agriculture in Scotland at this time.

2. How important were improvements to housing for farming families in Scotland?   **3**

Marks

SECTION B: ENQUIRY SKILLS

The issue for investigating is:

> Working conditions in the textile industry between 1750 and 1850 were better before the introduction of the factory system.

Study the sources carefully and answer the questions which follow.
You should use your own knowledge where appropriate.

Source C is from the diary of David Gilmour of Paisley, written in 1830, describing the lives of the handloom weavers around 1790.

Source C

> Every weaver, being his own master, came and went whenever he wished. When he took a day's holiday he made up for it before or after as it pleased him. The loom was his own property and he was answerable to his employer only.

3. How useful is **Source C** for investigating conditions for workers in the textile industry between 1750 and 1850?

3

Source D is from a letter in a parliamentary report published in 1840.

Source D

> Many people are mistaken about the extent to which factory labour is bad for the health of workers. I have seen handloom weavers working in cellars dug out of a swamp with water running down the bare walls.
>
> The factory worker has the exercise of walking to and from the factory and weaving in a large, roomy apartment in which the air is regularly changed.

4. What evidence in **Source C** agrees with the view that working conditions in the textile industry were better before the introduction of the factory system?

   What evidence in **Source D** disagrees with the view that working conditions in the textile industry were better before the introduction of the factory system?

5

5. How far do you agree that the working conditions in the textile industry were better before the introduction of the factory system? Use evidence from the sources and your own knowledge to come to a conclusion.

4

[END OF CONTEXT IA]

Mark

UNIT I—CHANGING LIFE IN SCOTLAND AND BRITAIN

CONTEXT B: 1830s–1930s

SECTION A: KNOWLEDGE AND UNDERSTANDING

Study the information in the sources. You must also use your own knowledge in your answers.

Source A is from "Change in Scotland" by W. Doran and R. Dargie.

Source A

> The coming of the railways brought new opportunities to many people in Scotland. People living in towns were able to get fresh food and milk from the country. Food manufacturers were able to sell their products further afield. Newspaper publishers increased their sales. Towns began to grow in size.

1. Describe some of the benefits railways brought to people living in towns.   4

In **Source B** Nellie Edgar describes her family's new council house in Glasgow.

Source B

> My parents' room was the parlour too, so they had their bed in it and a three piece suite. As well as that, we had a real living room separate from the kitchen, and a bathroom. No more tin tubs, and there was the garden.

2. How important were council houses in providing better living conditions after the First World War?   3

Marks

SECTION B: ENQUIRY SKILLS

The issue for investigating is:

> Machinery greatly improved coal mining by the 1930s.

Study the sources carefully and answer the questions which follow.
You should use your own knowledge where appropriate.

Source C is from "A Short History of the Scottish Coal-Mining Industry", published by The National Coal Board, Scottish Division in 1958.

Source C

> By the 1930s there had been great progress in power machinery which cut and loaded the coal mechanically. This means that mining could be carried out efficiently and with greater safety and that made for greater productivity than in the days of pick, shovel and pit pony.

3. How useful is **Source C** for investigating the effects of machinery on coal mining? 3

Source D is from a Royal Commission Report on Safety in Mines, published in the 1930s.

Source D

> Machines themselves involve risks due to their moving parts when at work. They also make it difficult to move, especially at the coal face, and they make a lot of noise. The more rapid advance of the coal face has caused an increase in the amount of gas and coal dust produced.

4. What evidence in **Source C** agrees with the view that machinery had greatly improved coal mining by the 1930s?

   What evidence in **Source D** disagrees with the view that machinery had greatly improved coal mining by the 1930s? 5

5. How far do you agree that machinery had greatly improved coal mining by the 1930s? Use evidence from the sources and your own knowledge to come to a conclusion. 4

[END OF CONTEXT IB]

UNIT I—CHANGING LIFE IN SCOTLAND AND BRITAIN

CONTEXT C: 1880s–Present Day

SECTION A: KNOWLEDGE AND UNDERSTANDING

Study the information in the sources. You must also use your own knowledge in your answers.

In **Source A** Bert Murray describes work done by women in Aberdeen during the Second World War.

Source A

> Women began to take over more of the jobs previously done by men. They took over jobs in civil defence and the fire service. They learned to drive various vehicles and worked in heavy and light industry.

1. Describe some of the work done by women during the Second World War.   **4**

Source B describes changes in housing in the countryside since the 1880s.

Source B

> Farmers were forced to provide better housing to stop their workers moving to the towns. Rows of reasonably solid cottages, most with running water, had appeared on every farm. By the end of the nineteenth century the standard of living of the average farm worker had improved.

2. How important have improvements in country housing been since 1880?   **3**

Marks

SECTION B: ENQUIRY SKILLS

The issue for investigating is:

> New technology has brought success to British shipbuilding since the Second World War.

Study the sources carefully and answer the questions which follow. You should use your own knowledge where appropriate.

Source C is from a recent book on industry in Britain by Watt and James.

Source C

> Construction of British ships uses the latest technology. Welding has replaced riveting. Prefabrication means that building can be done in indoor sheds. New forms of propulsion mean that British ships are fit to sail anywhere. British shipbuilding can compete on price, quality and delivery.

3. How useful is **Source C** for investigating the state of shipbuilding since the Second World War?   **3**

Source D describes the decline of Scottish shipbuilding.

Source D

> The shipyards of the Clyde built some of the best ships in the world. Now, despite new techniques and improved materials, some shipyards are not able to go on working. New methods, such as welding instead of riveting, have failed to meet the threat from foreign competitors.

4. What evidence is there in **Source C** that technology has brought success to British shipbuilding?

   What evidence is there in **Source D** that technology has not brought success to British shipbuilding?   **5**

5. How far do you agree that new technology has brought success to British shipbuilding since the Second World War? Use evidence from the sources and your own knowledge to come to a conclusion.   **4**

[END OF CONTEXT IC]

UNIT II—INTERNATIONAL COOPERATION AND CONFLICT

> CONTEXT A: 1790s–1820s

SECTION A: KNOWLEDGE AND UNDERSTANDING

Study the information in the sources. You must also use your own knowledge in your answers.

The following sources give evidence about the outbreak of war in Europe.

Source A gives a historian's view of Emperor Leopold's actions after the Flight to Varennes.

Source A

> The flight to Varennes was the first step on the road to war. Believing that Louis and Marie Antoinette were now in danger, Emperor Leopold promised to help them regain their liberty and their power. Then with the King of Prussia he called on all European kings to take action to help Louis.

1. Describe the actions of Emperor Leopold after the Flight to Varennes.   **3**

Source B is a speech about the French threat by William Pitt, the Prime Minister.

Source B

> Many are the reasons which have persuaded us to enter into war. I have heard of wars of honour. The French have attempted to interfere in the government of this country, to arm our subjects against us and to criticise our king. This becomes on our side a war of honour.

2. Explain why Britain declared war on France in 1793.   **4**

Marks

SECTION B: ENQUIRY SKILLS

The following sources are about Napoleon's invasion of Russia.

Study the sources carefully and answer the questions which follow.
You should use your own knowledge where appropriate.

Source C is from a letter written by a soldier in the French Army in Russia.

Source C

> Most houses stand empty and roofless. The houses have been ruined or ransacked, the inhabitants have fled. The streets are full of dead horses that give off a terrible smell now that the hot weather has come.

3. How useful is **Source C** as evidence about Napoleon's invasion of Russia?   3

Source D is a diary entry by Napoleon's Master of Horses.

Source D

> We had hoped to take possession of horses from the countryside. In Russia there was no way we could do this. Horses, cattle, inhabitants had all fled and we found ourselves in the middle of a desert.

4. Compare the views of the invasion of Russia by Napoleon's army given in **Sources C** and **D**.   3

5. How fully do **Sources C** and **D** explain what happened when Napoleon invaded Russia? You should use your own knowledge and give reasons for your answer.   4

[END OF CONTEXT IIA]

UNIT II—INTERNATIONAL COOPERATION AND CONFLICT

CONTEXT B: 1890s–1920s

SECTION A: KNOWLEDGE AND UNDERSTANDING

Study the information in the sources. You must also use your own knowledge in your answers.

Source A is part of a speech by Gavrilo Princip at his trial for the killing of Archduke Franz Ferdinand and his wife on the 28th June 1914.

Source A

> I fired twice at Ferdinand from a distance of four or five paces. I tried to commit suicide but some police officers seized and struck me. They took me away covered in blood, to the police station. I am not a criminal, for I destroyed a bad man. I thought I was right.

1. Describe the assassinations at Sarajevo on the 28th June 1914.   3

Source B is taken from the book "Twentieth Century History" by Tony Howarth.

Source B

> The Austrian government blamed the killings on Serbia. Encouraged by Germany the Austrians decided to use the murders as an excuse to attack Serbia. After making unacceptable demands on the Serbian government, Austria declared war on them on 28 July 1914.

2. Why did the assassinations at Sarajevo lead to the First World War?   4

Marks

SECTION B: ENQUIRY SKILLS

The following sources are about Germany's reaction to the Treaty of Versailles.

**Study the sources carefully and answer the questions which follow.
You should use your own knowledge where appropriate.**

Source C is taken from Adolf Hitler's book "Mein Kampf", published in 1925. Hitler fought on the Western Front during the First World War.

Source C

> Each one of the points of the Treaty of Versailles should be fixed in the minds and hearts of the German people until sixty million men and women find their souls aflame with the feeling of rage and shame. The common cry must be – "We will be armed again!"

3. How useful is **Source C** as evidence of how Germans felt about the Treaty of Versailles?   3

Source D was written by a British member of the Peace Conference at Versailles after the First World War.

Source D

> The German delegation was led by Count Brockdorff-Rantzau. He was so shocked that he could not stand to make his speech. In it he said "We have been forced to admit that we alone are guilty of causing the war; such an admission from me would be wrong".

4. To what extent do **Sources C** and **D** agree about the German attitude to the Treaty of Versailles?   3

Source E was written by Sir Phillip Gibbs who was a British representative at the Peace Conference.

Source E

> It was a peace of vengeance. It was very unfair. The economic terms of the treaty were mad. Germany had to pay for all the damage caused during the war. The impossibility of getting all this money from a defeated country was obvious even to the most ignorant schoolboy.

5. How far do you agree with the author of **Source E** that Germany was unfairly treated at the Peace Conference? Use evidence from the source and your own knowledge to come to a conclusion.   4

[END OF CONTEXT IIB]

UNIT II—INTERNATIONAL COOPERATION AND CONFLICT

CONTEXT C: 1930s–1960s

SECTION A: KNOWLEDGE AND UNDERSTANDING

Study the information in the sources. You must also use your own knowledge in your answers.

In **Source A** Hitler discusses his plans for the expansion of Germany.

Source A

> We cannot expect a repetition of Czechoslovakia. Poland will always be on the side of our enemies. We must attack Poland. We must crush Poland so that we can expand our Nazi state. Germans must have more living space in the East.

1. Describe Hitler's plans for expansion.   **3**

Source B is about France and Britain's reaction to Hitler's plan to invade Poland.

Source B

> France and Britain promised to help Poland if she was attacked. To do this they tried to make a pact with Russia, but Russia did not trust France and Britain. Russia also wanted to expand and made a pact with Hitler instead.

2. What were the results of the British and French plans to help Poland?   **4**

SECTION B: ENQUIRY SKILLS

The following sources are about international relations after the Second World War.

Study the sources carefully and answer the questions which follow.
You should use your own knowledge where appropriate.

In **Source C** a member of the United Nations Organisation gives his views on the Organisation in the late 1940s.

Source C

> The Great Powers must control the future. We can no longer permit any nation to settle their arguments with guns. We look to the future with confidence. Sensible discussion is the way ahead.

3. How useful is **Source C** as evidence about the United Nations?   3

Source D gives the views of another member of the United Nations.

Source D

> The Great Powers no longer matter. The world is now controlled by fear of the atomic bomb. No sooner had the Charter been signed than it was out of date. The balance of fear between the USA and the USSR is all that will matter.

4. To what extent do **Sources C** and **D** agree about the United Nations?   3

Source E describes the work of the United Nations Organisation.

Source E

> In 1946 there was a mood of determination, even desperation, to make sure that world war should not happen again. Education, health, justice became a part of the United Nations Charter for international peacekeeping. There have been many conflicts since, but none on a global scale.

5. How fully does **Source E** describe the work of the United Nations since 1946? You should use your own knowledge and give reasons for your answer.   4

[END OF CONTEXT IIC]

Mark

UNIT III—PEOPLE AND POWER

CONTEXT A: USA 1850–1880

SECTION A: KNOWLEDGE AND UNDERSTANDING

Study the information in the sources. You must also use your own knowledge in your answers.

Source A describes some of the difficulties of travelling by wagon train.

Source A

> Some were poorly prepared for such a journey and many joining us had little or nothing with them, so already small rations had to be divided. We had many weeks of bad weather, and our ox teams, being insufficient to pull the loads, made travelling over those prairies almost impossible. The young, and even old people, were forced to walk much of the way.

1. Describe some of the problems faced by people travelling by wagon train.   **3**

Source B deals with the Confederate attack on Fort Sumter.

Source B

> The Confederate attack on the Northern garrison in Fort Sumter was the clear sign that the war had begun.
>
> Yet when the fort was attacked this simply confirmed decisions which the leaders of the North and South, Lincoln and Davis, had already made. Both men had made up their minds to fight rather than to give in and each man had come to see Fort Sumter as the place for the show-down.

2. Explain why the attack on Fort Sumter began the American Civil War.   **3**

Marks

SECTION B: ENQUIRY SKILLS

The following sources are about westward expansion and its effects on the American Indians.

Study the sources carefully and answer the questions which follow.
You should use your own knowledge where appropriate.

Source C was written by Horace Greeley who travelled westwards across America in 1859.

Source C

> The Indians of the prairies are a disgrace. As I passed over those magnificent lands of Kansas which form the reservations of Indian tribes, I saw the very best corn lands on earth. And I saw their owners sitting around the doors of their lodges at the height of the planting season. I could not help saying: "These people must die out – there is no hope for them. God has given this land to those whose destiny is to conquer and cultivate it."

3. What are Horace Greeley's views of the American Indian?   4

In **Source D** Chief Joseph of the Nez Perces tribe describes the attitude of the American Indian to the land.

Source D

> My father sent for me as he was dying and said: "My son, my body is returning to Mother Earth. Always remember that your father never sold his country. You cannot sell what is not yours to give.
>
> However, a few more years, and white men will be all around you. They have their eyes on this land. My son, never forget my dying words. This country holds your father's body. Never sell the bones of your father."

4. Compare the different views towards the land in **Sources C** and **D**.   4

[END OF CONTEXT IIIA]

Mark.

UNIT III—PEOPLE AND POWER

CONTEXT B: INDIA 1917–1947

SECTION A: KNOWLEDGE AND UNDERSTANDING

Study the information in the sources. You must also use your own knowledge in your answers.

In **Source A** the Indian historian, K. K. Khullar, describes the events at Amritsar in 1919.

Source A

> The Jallianwalla Bagh (Amritsar) massacre was the idea of the governor of the Punjab, Sir Michael O'Dwyer, and not the actual man-in-charge, General Dyer. When the general ordered his men to open fire on unarmed civilians, he was following orders and he gave the crowd no warning.

1. Describe what happened at the Amritsar Massacre in 1919.   3

Source B describes Gandhi's "Passive Resistance" tactics.

Source B

> Gandhi had been successful in his new methods of Satyagraha (love-force) on behalf of farmers in Bihar in 1917 and he decided to use the same tactics against the British. The non-violent, non-cooperation movement worked well for six months in 1921 but there were still riots and it was suspended.

2. What were the results of Gandhi's "Passive Resistance" tactics?   3

Marks

SECTION B: ENQUIRY SKILLS

The sources are about religious and social divisions amongst Indians.

Study the sources carefully and answer the questions which follow.
You should use your own knowledge where appropriate.

In **Source C** an Indian author gives his opinion on the caste system.

Source C

> Hindus are labelled and suffer because of their caste. The caste system makes some people slaves and it divides Indian society. Until it is totally destroyed all Indians will never be equal and the country will not be united. The caste system was created by a few selfish people for their own benefit and they keep it in existence by calling it a religion.

3. What does the author of **Source C** think of the caste system?   4

Source D is about Hindus and Muslims in India.

Source D

> There were 255 million Hindus and 92 million Muslims in British India. The hatred between them came largely from their different religions.
>
> Hindus live according to a system of class and caste. Muslims believe that everyone is equal. But in India by the 1940s, almost all Muslims were the descendants of people from the lower castes of Hindu society. Muslims now had a caste system of their own.
>
> All these divisions added to tensions in India and prevented united action towards independence.

4. To what extent does **Source D** agree with **Source C** about religious divisions in India?   4

[END OF CONTEXT IIIB]

Marks

UNIT III—PEOPLE AND POWER

CONTEXT C: RUSSIA 1914–1941

SECTION A: KNOWLEDGE AND UNDERSTANDING

Study the information in the sources. You must also use your own knowledge in your answers.

In **Source A** Harry Mills describes Lenin's ideas.

Source A

> In April 1917 Lenin returned from exile and called on the Soviets to overthrow the Provisional Government. He said that the war must be ended. The peasants must be given their land. Food must be given to the hungry. These ideas were soon adopted and turned into popular slogans such as, "Peace, Bread and Land!"

1. Why did many people support Lenin and the Bolsheviks?   **3**

In **Source B** John Robottom describes the start of the Bolshevik Revolution in Petrograd in November 1917.

Source B

> Prime Minister Kerensky awoke on 7 November to be told that key places such as the power stations and the telephone exchange had been seized. Red Guards held the bridges over the river and they had captured the arsenal in the St Peter and Paul fortress.

2. Give a brief description of the Bolshevik takeover of power in Petrograd in November 1917.   **3**

SECTION B: ENQUIRY SKILLS

The following sources are about collectivisation and the kulaks.

Study the sources carefully and answer the questions which follow.
You should use your own knowledge where appropriate.

In **Source C** a young communist, who took part in the collectivisation of land under Stalin, describes events in one Russian village.

Source C

> A large crowd gathered outside the building. It was like a scene from a nightmare. In the background soldiers with revolvers drawn guarded about twenty young and old kulaks. A number of women and children were weeping hysterically. So this was how the kulaks were to be wiped out. A lot of simple peasants being sent to some distant labour camp.

3. What does the author of **Source C** think of the way kulaks were treated? Give reasons for your answer.   **4**

Source D is taken from a speech by Stalin about the treatment of the kulaks.

Source D

> We must smash the kulaks. We must strike at the kulaks so hard as to prevent them rising to their feet again. We must show no mercy and wipe them out as a social class.

4. To what extent do **Sources C** and **D** agree about the treatment of the kulaks?   **4**

[END OF CONTEXT IIIC]

Mark

UNIT III—PEOPLE AND POWER

CONTEXT D: GERMANY 1918–1939

SECTION A: KNOWLEDGE AND UNDERSTANDING

Study the information in the sources. You must also use your own knowledge in your answers.

Source A was written by someone who lived in Germany in the early 1920s.

Source A

> All the German people knew was that a large bank account could not buy a bunch of carrots, a few ounces of sugar, a pound of flour. They knew they were bankrupt, and they knew hunger when it struck them every day.

1. What were the results of the economic crisis of 1923 for the German people?   **3**

Source B is about the Munich Putsch.

Source B

> In Bavaria, Hitler and General von Ludendorff saw a chance to overthrow the Bavarian Government in Munich. Their rising began in a beer cellar where the Bavarian governor, von Kahr, was making a speech. The Nazis then marched towards the town centre.

2. Describe the events of the Munich Putsch of November 1923.   **3**

Marks

SECTION B: ENQUIRY SKILLS

The following sources are about the treatment of the Jews in Nazi Germany.

Study the sources carefully and answer the questions which follow.
You should use your own knowledge where appropriate.

Source C is from the American newspaper, "The New York Times", in November 1938.

Source C

> Huge crowds watched the destruction of the Jewish shops. Generally they were silent and most people seemed disturbed by what was happening. Only members of the wrecking squads shouted abuse at the Jews, although one person in the crowd shouted "Why not hang the owner in the window!". On the other hand, crowds have helped Jews escape from their shops unharmed.

3. What were the attitudes of people in Germany to the treatment of Jews as shown in **Source C**?   4

Source D is part of a report from Germany in 1938.

Source D

> The violence against the Jews has caused great concern among the people. People spoke their mind quite openly, and many Aryans were arrested as a result. Many people are looking after Jewish women and children by putting them up in their homes, while others are shopping for them, because it is forbidden to sell food to them.

4. To what extent do **Sources C** and **D** agree about the attitude of ordinary Germans towards the Jews?   4

[END OF CONTEXT IIID]

[END OF QUESTION PAPER]

[BLANK PAGE]

[BLANK PAGE]

[BLANK PAGE]

G

1540/402

NATIONAL QUALIFICATIONS 2000

TUESDAY, 6 JUNE
G/C 9.00 AM – 10.30 AM
F/G 10.20 AM – 11.50 AM

HISTORY STANDARD GRADE
General Level

Answer questions from Unit I **and** Unit II **and** Unit III.

Choose only **one** Context from each Unit and answer Sections A **and** B. The Contexts chosen should be those you have studied.

The Contexts in each Unit are:

You must use the information in the sources, and your own knowledge, to answer the questions.

Number the questions as shown in the question paper.

Some sources have been adapted or translated.

SCOTTISH QUALIFICATIONS AUTHORITY

Mark

UNIT I—CHANGING LIFE IN SCOTLAND AND BRITAIN

CONTEXT A: 1750s–1850s

SECTION A: KNOWLEDGE AND UNDERSTANDING

Study the information in the sources. You must also use your own knowledge in your answers.

Source A is from a speech given by Colonel Macleod in 1792.

Source A

> Most wealthy, male land-owners in Scotland can vote but there are many owners of large estates who do not own enough property and are deprived of their right to elect their Members of Parliament. This reduces the electors to a very small number. By the well-known invention of creating fictitious voters, the right of choosing MPs has been given to some small estate owners.

1. Who could vote for a Member of Parliament in 1792?   **4**

Source B gives evidence about Scotland's changing population.

Source B

> In 1750 Scotland was a rural society. Less than ten per cent of the population lived in towns. By 1850 almost a third did so. The growing urban areas had become the most important presence in Scotland. They were centres of industry and employment for both evicted farmers and Highlanders affected by the Clearances.

2. Explain why Scotland's population shifted to the towns in the period 1750–1850.   **3**

Marks

SECTION B: ENQUIRY SKILLS

The issue for investigating is:

> Rural housing in Scotland improved during the years 1750–1850.

Study the sources carefully and answer the questions which follow.
You should use your own knowledge where appropriate.

Source C is from William Cobbett's "Tour in Scotland" written in 1833.

Source C

> The Lowland farmer's house has changed from the simple, dirt-floored hut of past times. It is now big enough for a gentleman to live in. Its stone walls, large chimney and slate roof stand solidly in front of a farm yard with buildings on the side of it for horses, cattle and implements.

3. How useful is **Source C** for investigating improvements in rural housing during the years 1750–1850?   **3**

Source D was written by Hugh Miller about a visit to the Highlands in 1824.

Source D

> We entered through the turf and peat walls of the cottage and plunging downward we found ourselves in the dunghill which occupied a small room of the house also used for animals. We came upon an inner door and went in to the smoky interior where the inmates sat. The fire was placed in the middle of the earthen floor with a large pot of potatoes hanging above it.

4. What evidence in **Source C** agrees with the view that rural housing in Scotland improved during the years 1750–1850?

   What evidence in **Source D** disagrees with the view that rural housing in Scotland improved in the years 1750–1850?   **5**

5. How far do you agree that rural housing in Scotland improved during the years 1750–1850? You must use **evidence from the sources** and **your own knowledge** to come to a conclusion.   **4**

[END OF CONTEXT IA]

UNIT I—CHANGING LIFE IN SCOTLAND AND BRITAIN

CONTEXT B: 1830s–1930s

SECTION A: KNOWLEDGE AND UNDERSTANDING

Study the information in the sources. You must also use your own knowledge in your answers.

Source A is from "Changing Lives" by Sydney Wood.

Source A

> Mrs Pankhurst gathered around her women with the ability to speak at large meetings and organise processions and gatherings. When nothing happened, the WSPU turned to more noisy and forceful methods. They tried to spoil the meetings of Prime Minister Asquith and also smashed windows and set fire to the contents of letter boxes.

1. Describe the militant tactics used by suffragettes to try to gain the vote for women.   **4**

Source B is a description written by someone living in Glasgow in 1838.

Source B

> There are people who have come to Glasgow from as far as 60 miles away. My own father was a farmer in the Lothians. He was driven out by improvements in farming so he became a mechanic and settled in Glasgow. When small farms disappeared, many cottagers were driven out and they moved to the large towns.

2. Why did so many Scottish people move to large towns in the nineteenth century?   **3**

Marks

SECTION B: ENQUIRY SKILLS

The issue for investigating is:

> Housing conditions in rural areas of Scotland had not greatly improved by 1918.

Study the sources carefully and answer the questions which follow.
You should use your own knowledge where appropriate.

Source C is from a Royal Commission report on housing in Scotland, written in 1918.

Source C

> We have found many unsatisfactory sites of houses and villages and also badly constructed, damp labourers' cottages on many farms. In addition, we have come across insufficient supplies of water, bad drainage, inadequate removal of refuse and a lack of decent sanitary conditions. In the crofting counties and the islands we found whole townships unfit for human occupation.

3. How useful is **Source C** for investigating rural housing conditions in Scotland up to 1918?   3

Source D is from a modern history book.

Source D

> By 1870 some farmers had been forced to provide better housing for their workers. Rows of reasonably solid, stone or brick cottages had appeared on many farms. The rain could not enter through the well-constructed slate roofs and they had stone or wooden floors, a fireplace and a proper running water supply.

4. What evidence is there in **Source C** that rural housing conditions had not greatly improved by 1918?

    What evidence is there in **Source D** to show that rural housing conditions had improved by 1918?   5

5. How far do you think housing conditions in rural areas of Scotland had improved by 1918? You must use **evidence from the sources** and **your own knowledge** to come to a conclusion.   4

[END OF CONTEXT IB]

Mark

UNIT I—CHANGING LIFE IN SCOTLAND AND BRITAIN

CONTEXT C: 1880s–Present Day

SECTION A: KNOWLEDGE AND UNDERSTANDING

Study the information in the sources. You must also use your own knowledge in your answers.

Source A is from "Changing Lives" by Sydney Wood.

Source A

> Mrs Pankhurst gathered around her women with the ability to speak at large meetings and organise processions and gatherings. When nothing happened, the WSPU turned to more noisy and forceful methods. They tried to spoil the meetings of Prime Minister Asquith and also smashed windows and set fire to the contents of letter boxes.

1. Describe the militant tactics used by suffragettes to try to gain the vote for women.   **4**

Source B is about changes in population.

Source B

> The greatest change in Scotland between 1880 and 1980 was the size and population of towns. At the start of the period, people were coming from the countryside and from overseas to live in Scotland's towns. Thousands of people flocked into the bustling city centres looking for work.

2. Why did the population in towns in Scotland increase after 1880?   **3**

SECTION B: ENQUIRY SKILLS

The issue for investigating is:

> Council housing estates provided good living conditions by the 1940s.

Study the sources carefully and answer the questions which follow.
You should use your own knowledge where appropriate.

Source C is from a local council report on council housing, written in the 1940s.

Source C

> Wishaw Town Council has laid out new housing schemes where the houses have been built in pairs or in fours, all with gardens. The houses all have a living room, a bathroom and a kitchen and 2 or 3 bedrooms. Old slum houses have also been torn down and new council houses erected. Sometimes there are public parks and playing fields with swings, see-saws and sand-pits.

3. How useful is **Source C** for investigating the effects of council housing estates by the 1940s?   3

Source D describes council houses in the 1940s.

Source D

> These new houses were built as cheaply as possible to keep rents low. They were crammed into estates built on poor land near railway lines and gas works. They lacked shops and other facilities. The poorest families with the biggest problems were taken from the old slums and grouped together in these large council housing schemes.

4. What evidence is there in **Source C** to support the view that council housing estates provided good living conditions by the 1940s?

   What evidence is there in **Source D** that council housing estates did not provide good living conditions by the 1940s?   5

5. To what extent do you think council housing estates provided good living conditions by the 1940s? You must use **evidence from the sources** and **your own knowledge** to come to a conclusion.   4

[END OF CONTEXT IC]

UNIT II—INTERNATIONAL COOPERATION AND CONFLICT

CONTEXT A: 1790s–1820s

SECTION A: KNOWLEDGE AND UNDERSTANDING

Study the information in the sources. You must also use your own knowledge in your answers.

Source A gives details about the Battle of Leipzig in Northern Germany in October 1813.

Source A

	FRANCE	ALLIES
Commanded by	Napoleon	Schwarzenberg, Blucher, Bernadotte
Soldiers from	France, Poland, Germany	Austria, Russia, Prussia, Sweden
Size of Armies	177 500	332 000
Losses	68 000	54 000

1. Explain why the Allies were so successful in October 1813.   3

In **Source B** a modern historian describes the effects of the French Wars on the British people.

Source B

Half a million men were taken from working on the land or in industry to fight in the army and the navy. This caused delays in production and shortages of labour. Farmers and factory owners were forced to change to labour-saving machinery.

2. How important were employment problems for the British people during the wars with France?   4

Marks

SECTION B: ENQUIRY SKILLS

The following sources are about the Congress System.

Study the sources carefully and answer the questions which follow.
You should use your own knowledge where appropriate.

Source C is from a State paper written by Lord Castlereagh, British Foreign Secretary, in 1820.

Source C

> The Quadruple Alliance was set up to free the majority of Europe from the control of the French army. The Quadruple Alliance and the Congress System, which I created, now protect the states of Europe. This allows them to come together to settle matters which threaten European peace. It must not interfere in the internal affairs of these countries.

3. What was Castlereagh's attitude to the systems set up to deal with threats to European peace after 1815?   **4**

In **Source D** the historians Richards and Hunt explain Castlereagh's reasons for setting up the Congress System.

Source D

> Castlereagh thought up the Congress System. He thought that if all nations could meet together then the Great Powers might gradually learn to cooperate. Thus a military alliance against France became a permanent and bloodless method of settling the affairs of Europe.

4. Compare the evidence in **Sources C** and **D** on the systems set up to deal with threats to European peace after 1815.   **4**

[END OF CONTEXT IIA]

Mark

UNIT II—INTERNATIONAL COOPERATION AND CONFLICT

> ### CONTEXT B: 1890s–1920s

SECTION A: KNOWLEDGE AND UNDERSTANDING

Study the information in the sources. You must also use your own knowledge in your answers.

Source A is about the system of alliances in Europe before the First World War.

Source A

> The Alliance System caused Europe to be divided into two armed camps. The new German Empire formed an alliance with Austria-Hungary. That power bloc, stretching across Central Europe and later joined by Italy, became known as the Triple Alliance. This scared the French and the Russians.

1. What were the results of the system of alliances in Europe before the First World War?   **3**

Source B is about the employment of women during the First World War.

Source B

> No one would have dreamed of employing women bus conductors before the war but now they needed them. Women also found jobs on the railways, in shops and factories, and even as policewomen. In 1917, the Women's Land Army was formed to release male farm labourers for war work.

2. How important a role did women play during the First World War?   **4**

Marks

SECTION B: ENQUIRY SKILLS

The following sources are about the League of Nations.

**Study the sources carefully and answer the questions which follow.
You should use your own knowledge where appropriate.**

Source C gives extracts from the Covenant of the League of Nations.

Source C

> The aims of the League of Nations are to settle disputes among nations and prevent war.
>
> Members of the League recognise that keeping peace requires national armaments to be reduced.
>
> Any member country going to war against another member shall be said to have committed an act of war against all members of the League.
>
> All members shall immediately cut off all trade with any state which breaks the Covenant.

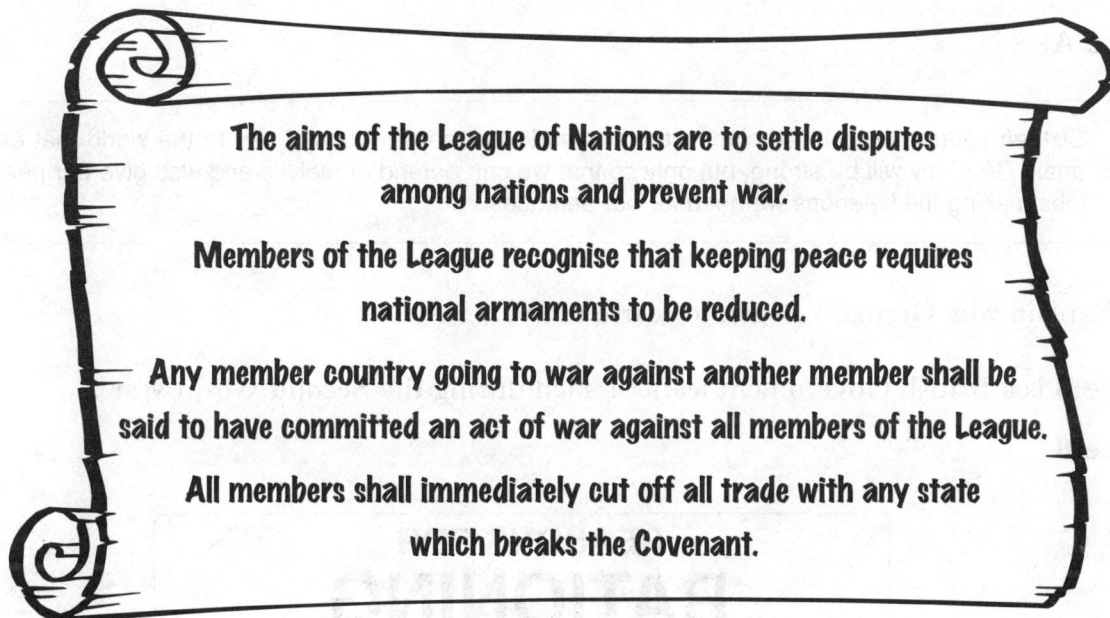

3. What are the views of the authors of the Covenant about what the League of Nations should do?

4

In **Source D** a modern historian describes some of the problems which faced the League of Nations.

Source D

> As a peace keeping body the League of Nations was a failure. An organisation which professed to be in favour of peace and prevent war still allowed its members to keep armaments. There was also a lack of will power to make it work. To take action against a member who broke the rules of the Covenant required all the member nations to act together and that rarely happened.

4. How far do **Sources C** and **D** agree about the League of Nations?

4

[END OF CONTEXT IIB]

Mark

UNIT II—INTERNATIONAL COOPERATION AND CONFLICT

CONTEXT C: 1930s–1960s

SECTION A: KNOWLEDGE AND UNDERSTANDING

Study the information in the sources. You must also use your own knowledge in your answers.

Source A is part of a speech by Adolf Hitler in March 1935.

Source A

> Sixteen years have passed since we were made to disarm. Today I say to the world that once again Germany will be strong, but only so that we can defend ourselves and also give our people jobs making the weapons we need for our defences.

1. Explain why Germany began to rearm in 1935.   **3**

Source B is a British Government leaflet issued during the Second World War.

Source B

REASONS FOR
RATIONING

1 RATIONING PREVENTS WASTE OF FOOD
   We must not ask our sailors to bring us unnecessary
   food cargoes at the risk of their lives.

2 RATIONING INCREASES OUR WAR EFFORT
   To reduce our purchases of food abroad is to
   release ships for bringing us other imports.

3 RATIONING DIVIDES SUPPLIES EQUALLY
   There will be ample supplies for our 44 million
   people but we must divide them fairly, everyone
   being treated alike.

2. How important was the introduction of rationing during the Second World War?   **4**

Marks

SECTION B: ENQUIRY SKILLS

The following sources are about the United Nations Organisation.

Study the sources carefully and answer the questions which follow.
You should use your own knowledge where appropriate.

Source C is from a speech by Stalin about Russian membership of the United Nations.

Source C

> Even as members, we do not trust the United Nations as a peace-keeping body. As a matter of fact, the UN is not a united, worldwide organisation formed to keep peace. It is an organisation for the Americans acting for the needs of American aggression.

3. What was Stalin's opinion of the United Nations?   4

Source D is by a modern historian.

Source D

> The increasing rivalry of the Soviet Union and the United States made many question how "united" the United Nations could be or how effective a peace-keeping body. Any permanent member could use its power of veto to block proposals. This meant that America or Russia would prevent important decisions from being made.

4. To what extent do **Sources C** and **D** agree about the United Nations?   4

[END OF CONTEXT IIC]

Mark

UNIT III—PEOPLE AND POWER

CONTEXT A: USA 1850–1880

SECTION A: KNOWLEDGE AND UNDERSTANDING

Study the information in the sources. You must also use your own knowledge in your answers.

Source A gives some evidence about Southern states seceding from the Union.

Source A

> At a state convention in Charleston, South Carolina voted to secede from the Union. This was the start which persuaded others. It was obvious that one small state could not go it alone. The cotton states, accordingly, followed suit and delegates from the break-away states met to set up a new nation.

1. Describe the ways in which the Southern states broke away from the Union in 1860–1861.   **3**

Source B is from a speech made by Abraham Lincoln to the people in the Southern states in March 1861.

Source B

> In your hands my dissatisfied fellow citizens and not in mine is the momentous issue of Civil War. You have no oath registered in heaven to destroy the existing government while I have made the most solemn oath to preserve, protect and defend it. We are not enemies but friends.

2. Explain why Lincoln was so anxious to prevent a Civil War.   **3**

SECTION B: ENQUIRY SKILLS

The following sources are about relationships between native Americans ("Indians") and white settlers in nineteenth-century America.

**Study the sources carefully and answer the questions which follow.
You should use your own knowledge where appropriate.**

Source C is an American artist's impression of a night attack by native Americans ("Indians") on a wagon train. It was drawn in 1877.

Source C

3. How useful is **Source C** as evidence of nineteenth-century white American attitudes towards the native Americans ("Indians")?   **3**

Source D is from "The Manners And Customs of the North American Indians" written by George Catlin in 1841.

Source D

> The character of the Indian is a simple one. They attack bravely and openly and only to protect their hunting grounds. The Indian is honest, brave and warlike but also honourable and religious. From the many acts of kindness I have received, I say they are a kind and hospitable people.

4. How far do **Sources C** and **D** agree about the native Americans ("Indians")?   **3**

Source E is from "Bridging a Continent" by the historian, Martin Hillman.

Source E

> The Americans who took part in Western expansion believed that the wilderness they roamed rightfully belonged to the United States. They believed that the Indians had no more claim to the land than the coyotes (wild dogs). The Indians were merely part of the landscape and just one of the obstacles that Americans had to overcome to fulfil their destiny.

5. How fully does **Source E** describe the white Americans' attitude to the native Americans ("Indians") in America between 1850 and 1880? You should use your own knowledge and give reasons for your answer.   **4**

[END OF CONTEXT IIIA]

Mark.

UNIT III—PEOPLE AND POWER

> ### CONTEXT B: INDIA 1917–1947

SECTION A: KNOWLEDGE AND UNDERSTANDING

Study the information in the sources. You must also use your own knowledge in your answers.

Source A describes the way Untouchables were treated.

Source A

> The Untouchables are completely outside the caste system of Hinduism. They live in slums and are confined to the unpleasant tasks of removing human waste and dead animals. High caste Indians consider themselves polluted if Untouchables drink from the same water well as they do.

1. Describe how the Untouchables were treated. **3**

Source B is from a letter written by Gandhi.

Source B

> I will tell you why I regard the British rule as a curse. British rule has reduced us to slavery. It has destroyed our culture. It seems clear as daylight that British statesmen will not make any change to British policy that might harm Britain's trade with India.

2. Why did Gandhi oppose British rule in India? **3**

Page sixteen

Marks

SECTION B: ENQUIRY SKILLS

The following sources are about British interests in India.

Study the sources carefully and answer the questions which follow.
You should use your own knowledge where appropriate.

Source C is an advertisement from "The Times" in London in 1926.

Source C

3. How useful is **Source C** as evidence of India's importance to Britain before 1939?   **3**

4. How fully does **Source C** explain why Britain wanted to keep control of India? You should use your own knowledge and give reasons for your answer.   **4**

Source D is from a speech by Winston Churchill in 1931.

Source D

> I do not believe the British people will agree to be pushed or persuaded out of India. No country has ever willingly given up something so valuable to her. There are British rights and interests in India. Years of hard work in building up trading and shipping links and establishing good government have achieved a great deal. Many lives have been spent in service to the Indian people themselves.

5. How far do **Sources C** and **D** agree about British interests in India?   **3**

[END OF CONTEXT IIIB]

UNIT III—PEOPLE AND POWER

> ### CONTEXT C: RUSSIA 1914–1941

SECTION A: KNOWLEDGE AND UNDERSTANDING

Study the information in the sources. You must also use your own knowledge in your answers.

Source A describes the unhappiness of the Russian people under the Provisional Government.

Source A

> Prime Minister Kerensky tried hard to keep up the spirits of the Russian army but failed. The German army was better equipped. Soon there were more defeats. Food prices at home continued to rise. Kerensky's promises seemed to be for the future. Lenin offered what the people wanted then and there.

1. Explain why there was discontent with the Provisional Government.   3

Source B describes the Red Army during the Civil War.

Source B

> The Reds controlled the heartland of Russia and all the internal lines of communication. Most ordinary Russians believed the Reds represented their interests in defending the Revolution. The Whites on the other hand were not united.

2. What advantages did the Red Army have over the Whites?   3

SECTION B: ENQUIRY SKILLS

The following sources are about Stalin's political purges during the 1930s.

Study the sources carefully and answer the questions which follow. You should use your own knowledge where appropriate.

In **Source C** Stalin proudly displays a pyramid of skulls of those who died in his purges. The cartoon was drawn in the 1930s by an anti-Communist living in France. The words say "Visit the USSR's pyramids".

Source C

3. How useful is **Source C** as evidence of the way in which Stalin dealt with opposition?   **3**

Source D is an eye witness account from someone sent to one of Stalin's labour camps.

Source D

> At the end of my first day, there were many corpses left on the work site. One worker was lying dead beneath an overturned wheelbarrow and two were frozen solid. At night the sledges went out and collected them all. In the summer, bones remained from corpses which had not been removed in time and the workers put them into the concrete mixer together with the cement.

4. To what extent do **Sources C** and **D** agree about the way Stalin dealt with opposition?   **3**

Source E is taken from a book called "Gulag Archipelago" which was written by a man who was in a labour camp.

Source E

> Ordinary Russians who spoke their minds against Stalin, or who were simply in the wrong class, made up most of Stalin's victims. However, Stalin also used the Secret Police against leading Communists. Having defeated his main rival, Trotsky, Stalin now wanted to remove all possible rivals.

5. How fully does **Source E** explain the reasons for Stalin's purges? You should use your own knowledge and give reasons for your answer.   **4**

[END OF CONTEXT IIIC]

Mark

UNIT III—PEOPLE AND POWER

CONTEXT D: GERMANY 1918–1939

SECTION A: KNOWLEDGE AND UNDERSTANDING

Study the information in the sources. You must also use your own knowledge in your answers.

In **Source A** a modern historian describes the Spartacist uprising.

Source A

> The Spartacists wanted Germany to have a Communist government like Russia. Ebert's government used armed force to crush this Communist rising in Berlin. Hundreds of Communists were slaughtered, including their leaders.

1. Describe the Spartacist uprising.   **3**

Source B is about Hitler's rise to power.

Source B

> The Depression had created the conditions for Hitler's rise to power. Hitler appealed to people's fears and hates and these emotions flourished in the hard times of the early 1930s. A brilliant master of the dark arts of propaganda, it was he who turned the Nazis into a party of the masses. Never far below the surface was also an element of brutality and control.

2. Explain why Hitler was so successful in winning power in Germany.   **3**

SECTION B: ENQUIRY SKILLS

The following sources are about opposition to Nazi government in the 1930s.

**Study the sources carefully and answer the questions which follow.
You should use your own knowledge where appropriate.**

Marks

Source C is a graph showing estimated numbers of prisoners in concentration camps in Germany taken from Nazi documents.

Source C

ESTIMATED NUMBERS OF PRISONERS IN NAZI CONCENTRATION CAMPS

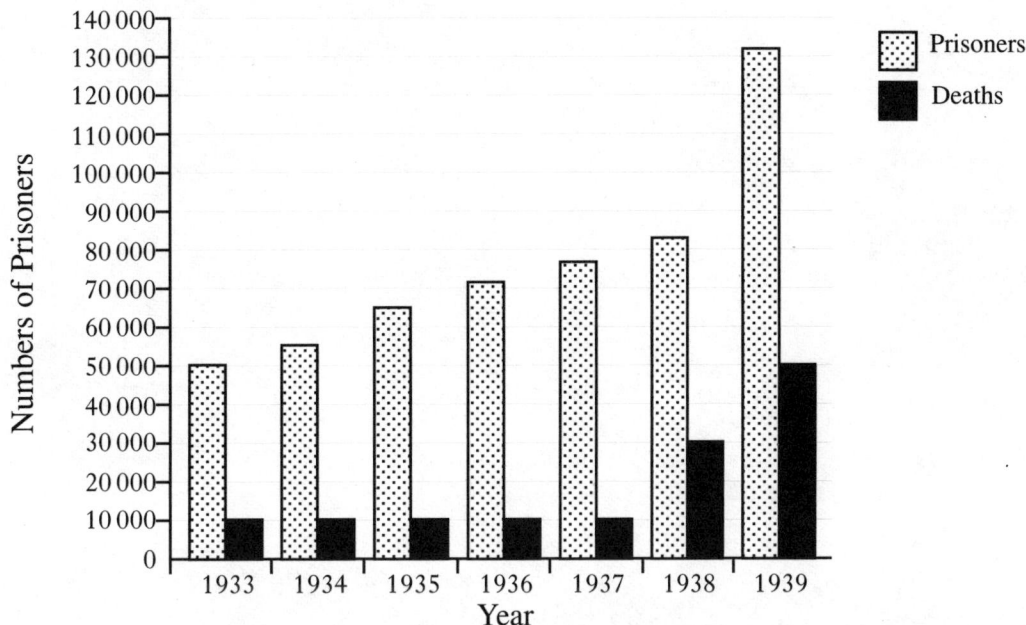

3. How useful is **Source C** for studying Nazi methods of dealing with opposition in the 1930s?

3

Source D was written by a former prisoner of a concentration camp.

Source D

> Every year from 1933 our numbers increased. In 1939 there were many thousands of us—all prisoners of the Nazis because we opposed their will. We made up a small part of the many thousands held in concentration camps throughout the Reich. Many of us were just poor devils accused of having spoken against the Fuhrer.

4. How far do **Sources C** and **D** agree about Nazi concentration camps?

3

In **Source E** an Englishwoman describes a conversation with a German army officer in 1936.

Source E

> I came away depressed. I know there are anti-Nazi groups in the Church and the Civil Service but they seem unable to do anything. The Nazis got a stranglehold before anyone realised what was happening. The Nazis seem to have enormous energy and power and the opposition groups don't seem to have either.

5. How fully does **Source E** explain why it was difficult to oppose the Nazis? You should use your own knowledge and give reasons for your answer.

4

[END OF CONTEXT IIID]
[END OF QUESTION PAPER]

[BLANK PAGE]

[BLANK PAGE]

[BLANK PAGE]

G

1540/402

NATIONAL QUALIFICATIONS 2001	WEDNESDAY, 30 MAY G/C 9.00 AM – 10.30 AM F/G 10.20 AM – 11.50 AM	**HISTORY STANDARD GRADE** General Level

Answer questions from Unit I **and** Unit II **and** Unit III.

Choose only **one** Context from each Unit and answer Sections A **and** B. The Contexts chosen should be those you have studied.

The Contexts in each Unit are:

You must use the information in the sources, and your own knowledge, to answer the questions.

Number the questions as shown in the question paper.

Some sources have been adapted or translated.

SCOTTISH QUALIFICATIONS AUTHORITY

©

Mark

UNIT I—CHANGING LIFE IN SCOTLAND AND BRITAIN

CONTEXT A: 1750s–1850s

SECTION A: KNOWLEDGE AND UNDERSTANDING

Study the information in the sources. You must also use your own knowledge in your answers.

Source A is a description of new farming methods.

Source A

> In Scotland the wind did not always blow when a farmer wanted it. So James Meikle invented a machine to winnow and thresh the grain whatever the weather might be. James Small invented a new plough with an iron blade. It could easily slice through the soil. It could be pulled by a pair of horses.

1. Explain in what ways the new farming inventions were better than the old methods.   **4**

Source B was written by Dr John Snow in 1854 about an outbreak of disease in London.

Source B

> The most terrible outbreak of cholera has broken out in Broad Street. I suspect that the water in the much used pump in the street has been contaminated (polluted). In the last, large epidemic of 1848 almost 50 000 died from cholera.

2. How important was it to provide good water supplies in Britain in the nineteenth century?   **3**

Marks

SECTION B: ENQUIRY SKILLS

The issue for investigating is:

> The population of Scotland rose between 1760 and 1820 as a result of improvements in food supply.

**Study the sources carefully and answer the questions which follow.
You should use your own knowledge where appropriate.**

Source C is from the autobiography of Thomas Somerville, a Scottish farmer. He wrote it in 1814.

Source C

> In the 1760s oat cakes formed the main food for my family. There was very little meat. Potatoes were still considered a luxury. The only vegetables grown were cabbages and turnips and they were of poor quality. People ate very little and very badly in my early life but now they eat much better. More babies are now born healthy and fewer die in their first months.

3. How useful is **Source C** for investigating causes of population growth in Scotland between 1760 and 1820?   **3**

Source D is from "Living in Scotland 1760–1820" by A. D. Cameron.

Source D

> The growth in population between 1750 and 1820 was caused by a rise in the birth rate. At this time of great economic change the demand for labour brought higher wages, earlier marriages and more births. There were also advances in hygiene and medical care.

4. What evidence in **Source C** agrees with the view that improvements in food supply caused a rise in the population?

   What evidence in **Source D** suggests that there were other reasons for population rise?   **5**

5. How far do you agree that the population of Scotland rose between 1750 and 1820 as a result of improvements in food supply?

   You must use evidence **from the sources** and **your own knowledge** to come to a conclusion.   **4**

[END OF CONTEXT IA]

Marks

UNIT I—CHANGING LIFE IN SCOTLAND AND BRITAIN

> ### CONTEXT B: 1830s–1930s

SECTION A: KNOWLEDGE AND UNDERSTANDING

Study the information in the sources. You must also use your own knowledge in your answers.

Source A describes some railway improvements made between 1850 and 1914.

Source A

> By the late 19th century, main line express trains increased their average speed to over 60 mph. In 1895 there was serious competition between the two railway companies on the London to Aberdeen route. The fastest did the 524 mile journey in eight and a half hours. Improved locomotives made these new speeds possible. Heating was gradually introduced into passenger trains.

1. Explain in what ways travelling by train improved between 1850 and 1930.   **4**

Source B describes problems caused by a lack of clean water in the nineteenth century.

Source B

> Typhus, carried by lice from unwashed bodies, killed many people in the slums. Typhoid fever and cholera also resulted from dirty food or contaminated (polluted) water. The terrifying cholera epidemics, such as those of 1831–1832 and 1849, killed over 100 000 people.

2. How important for people's health was a clean water supply in the nineteenth century?   **3**

Marks

SECTION B: ENQUIRY SKILLS

The issue for investigating is:

> A better diet during the nineteenth century resulted in an increase in the population.

Study the sources carefully and answer the questions which follow.
You should use your own knowledge where appropriate.

Source C was written by Samuel Robinson in 1872. It gives his memories of life in South West Scotland.

Source C

> What an amazing change in eating habits have the years brought about. We now have a baker or two in almost every village. Almost everyone can afford to buy fresh butcher meat and more vegetables and sugar. This has produced a change in the health of the whole community. People now live longer and have larger families.

3. How useful is **Source C** for investigating causes of population growth in Scotland during the nineteenth century?

3

Source D is from "Nineteenth Century British History" by Michael Lynch, published in 1999.

Source D

> The main cause of the declining death rate was the drop in infant mortality (deaths). Children survived to become adults as a result of general improvement in the standard of people's health. Mothers were healthier and gave birth to healthier babies, more of whom survived.

4. What evidence in **Source C** supports the view that a better diet led to an increase in the population?

   What evidence in **Source D** reveals other reasons for an increase in the population?

5

5. How far do you agree that a better diet led to the growth of population in nineteenth century Scotland?

   You must use evidence **from the sources** and **your own knowledge** to come to a conclusion.

4

[END OF CONTEXT IB]

UNIT I—CHANGING LIFE IN SCOTLAND AND BRITAIN

CONTEXT C: 1880s–Present Day

SECTION A: KNOWLEDGE AND UNDERSTANDING

Study the information in the sources. You must also use your own knowledge in your answers.

Source A describes changes which motor transport has made to the countryside.

Source A

> Motor transport now takes villagers to the town. Children are collected by school bus. The town doctor's practice extends into the countryside. On the other hand, every beauty spot has been ruined by the need to build roads.

1. Explain in what ways motor transport affected the lives of people living in the countryside.

    4

Source B describes improvements to water supply.

Source B

> It was far better to stop disease from spreading by tackling their causes such as dirty water contaminated (polluted) by sewage. Water was cleaned up and by 1900 most towns had a clean supply. Proper sewage systems were built. Pipes and tunnels were laid to take waste to places where it was treated.

2. How important was clean water to the improvement of health in towns?

    3

SECTION B: ENQUIRY SKILLS

The issue for investigating is:

> A better diet has led to the growth of the population in Scottish towns.

Study the sources carefully and answer the questions which follow.
You should use your own knowledge where appropriate.

Source C is from a volume of the "Third Statistical Account of Scotland", written in 1960.

Source C

> The population of the main towns in Aberdeenshire has grown in the last 30 years. The town dwellers are better fed. They have more money to spend on food. They get more fruit when very small and also proper school meals and free milk. Most important of all, the milk has been cleaned up. Forty years ago it was common to find a sediment at the bottom of a glass of milk, but not now.

3. How useful is **Source C** for investigating the reasons for population growth in Scottish towns?   3

Source D is from "People and Society in Scotland, 1914–1990", published in 1992.

Source D

> During the period 1920–1960 more babies lived to the age of one and beyond. Fewer young adults died of tuberculosis. The major reason for this was the development of antibiotics. Less women died during childbirth and went on to have families.

4. What evidence is there in **Source C** that a better diet led to the growth of population?

    What evidence is there in **Source D** that other factors led to the growth of population?   5

5. How far do you agree that a better diet led to the growth of population in Scottish towns?

    You must use evidence **from the sources** and **your own knowledge** to come to a conclusion.   4

[END OF CONTEXT IC]

UNIT II—INTERNATIONAL COOPERATION AND CONFLICT

CONTEXT A: 1790s–1820s

SECTION A: KNOWLEDGE AND UNDERSTANDING

Study the information in the sources. You must also use your own knowledge in your answers.

Source A deals with the British Navy's attacks on the French fleet in 1798.

Source A

> Napoleon avoided Nelson and landed in Egypt where he defeated the Turkish army in the Battle of the Pyramids. Then Nelson, who had been sailing up and down the Mediterranean, destroyed the French fleet at the Battle of Aboukir Bay. Britain had gained naval control in the Mediterranean and occupied the island of Minorca.

1. How important was Nelson to Britain's victory in the war at sea?   **3**

Source B describes some of the hardships faced by sailors during the Revolutionary Wars.

Source B

> The sailors' diet was badly balanced and this led to outbreaks of scurvy. This caused the sufferer's gums to swell, his teeth to fall out and swellings and sores to appear on his body. On the lower decks there was little fresh air, and the air was damp. The hammocks, often soaking, were jammed together. There were no washing facilities.

2. Describe conditions for British sailors serving on warships during the Revolutionary Wars.   **4**

SECTION B: ENQUIRY SKILLS

The following sources are about the effect of war on French civilians.

Study the sources carefully and answer the questions which follow.
You should use your own knowledge where appropriate.

Source C describes problems facing France during the Revolutionary Wars.

Source C

> The French people were worried that the war was going against them. Another major concern was the high price of food. Prices were rising because, to pay for the war, the government was printing huge amounts of paper money. But the more bank notes were printed, the less they were worth. By 1793, angry French people found that a bank note was only worth half the amount printed on it.

3. According to the author of **Source C** what were the opinions of French people during the Revolutionary Wars?

    3

Source D is from "European History 1789–1914" by C. A. Leeds.

Source D

> During the Revolutionary War France was in the midst of famine and lawlessness. Unemployment was high as industry had collapsed. Marat observed that the war was needed to "rid France of 300 000 armed criminals."

4. How fully does **Source D** describe the difficulties facing the French during the Revolutionary War?

    You should use **your own knowledge** and give reasons for your answer.

    4

[END OF CONTEXT IIA]

UNIT II—INTERNATIONAL COOPERATION AND CONFLICT

CONTEXT B: 1890s–1920s

SECTION A: KNOWLEDGE AND UNDERSTANDING

Study the information in the sources. You must also use your own knowledge in your answers.

In **Source A** George Coppard describes his experiences of the First World War.

Source A

> The battalion moved up the communication trench to the front line trench at a snail's pace, suffering heavy casualties from shrapnel fire. We passed stretcher bearers with the many wounded and groups of tired troops going to the rear. We would soon be in the attack on the German front line.

1. What methods of fighting were used on the Western Front in the First World War?   **4**

Source B is from a biography of Georges Clemenceau who represented France at the Treaty of Versailles.

Source B

> Clemenceau was a firm believer in the view that you must not negotiate with a German; you must dictate to him; on no other terms will a German respect you. Clemenceau was convinced that the negotiators at Versailles had to treat Germany firmly. He had twice seen his beloved France invaded by Germans in his lifetime. He was determined it must never happen again.

2. How important were Clemenceau's views on how Germany should be treated after the First World War?

3

Marks

SECTION B: ENQUIRY SKILLS

The following sources are about the effects of the First World War on German civilians.

Study the sources carefully and answer the questions which follow.
You should use your own knowledge where appropriate.

Source C is a German poster from 1918. It has been translated into English.

Source C

> # BRITAIN'S THE CAUSE!
>
> - **WHY ARE WE STILL FIGHTING?**
> - **WHY DO WE HAVE TO SCRIMP AND SAVE?**
> - **WHY CAN'T WE GO ABOUT OUR ORDINARY LIFE IN PEACE?**
>
> ## BECAUSE BRITAIN IS OUR DEADLY ENEMY.
>
> - **LET US GO FORWARD IN STRENGTH TOGETHER.**
> - **WE CAN STILL GUARANTEE VICTORY FOR GERMANY.**

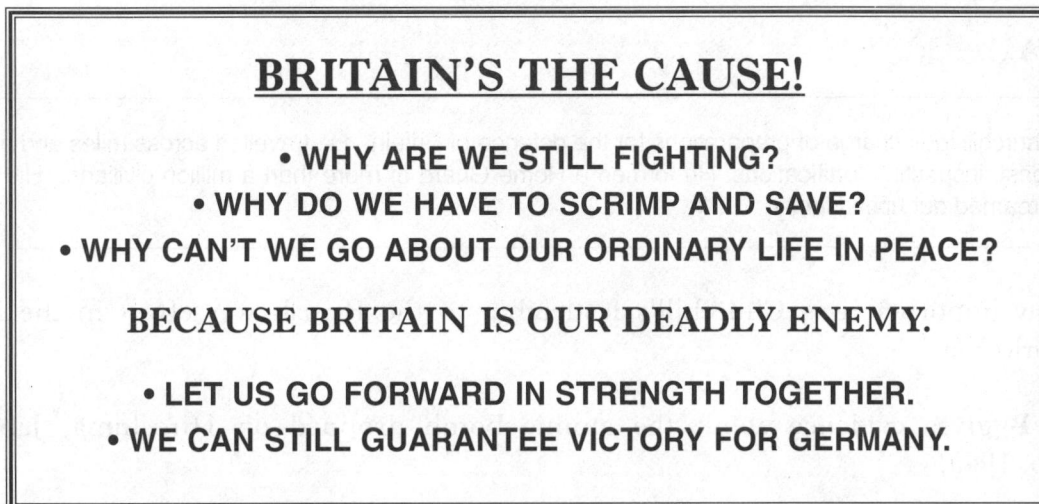

3. What opinions does the poster (**Source C**) want German people to have?   3

In **Source D**, the historian, John Keegan, describes Germany during war time.

Source D

> The winter of 1916–1917 became the "turnip winter" when that tasteless and unnutritious root appeared as a substitute or an additive at most meals. Luxuries, particularly coffee, disappeared from the tables of all but the rich. Real necessities like soap were strictly rationed.

4. How fully does **Source D** show the difficulties faced by German civilians in the First World War?

   You should use **your own knowledge** and give reasons for your answer.   4

[*END OF CONTEXT IIB*]

UNIT II—INTERNATIONAL COOPERATION AND CONFLICT

> **CONTEXT C: 1930s–1960s**

SECTION A: KNOWLEDGE AND UNDERSTANDING

Study the information in the sources. You must also use your own knowledge in your answers.

Source A describes Winston Churchill's leadership of Britain in 1940.

Source A

> Churchill took charge of preparations for the defence of Britain. He travelled across miles and miles of coast, inspecting fortifications. He formed a Home Guard of more than a million civilians. His orders streamed out unceasingly.

1. How important was Churchill's leadership to the British war effort in the Second World War?   **3**

Source B gives evidence about the atomic bomb dropped on Hiroshima, Japan, on August 6, 1945.

Source B

> There was a glaring, pinkish light in the sky which burned people's eyes out. Anyone within a kilometre of the explosion became a bundle of smoking black charcoal within seconds. Within minutes about 70 000 people were dead.

2. What were the effects of the dropping of the atomic bomb on Hiroshima?   **4**

SECTION B: ENQUIRY SKILLS

The following sources are about the effects of the war on German civilians.

Study the sources carefully and answer the questions which follow.
You should use your own knowledge where appropriate.

In **Source C** a German woman living in Hamburg in 1943 describes the aftermath of a British air raid.

Source C

> The following morning all women and children had to be evacuated from the city. It was dreadful. There was no gas, no electricity, not a drop of water. It is hard to imagine the panic and the chaos. We had only one idea: to escape.

3. According to **Source C**, what was the attitude of Germans living in Hamburg towards air raids?   3

Source D is from a leaflet published by German students in Munich in 1943.

Source D

> The war is approaching its certain end. Hitler cannot win the war but only extend it. Germans! Break with everything to do with Nazism before it is too late. A German victory cannot be achieved by criminals. Support the resistance movement; distribute this leaflet.

4. How fully does **Source D** describe the feelings of German civilians during the war?

    You should use **your own knowledge** and give reasons for your answer.   4

[END OF CONTEXT IIC]

Mark

UNIT III—PEOPLE AND POWER

CONTEXT A: USA 1850–1880

SECTION A: KNOWLEDGE AND UNDERSTANDING

Study the information in the sources. You must also use your own knowledge in your answers.

In **Source A** a Blackfoot native American chief talks about the importance of land.

Source A

> Our land is more valuable than your white man's money. It will not perish by the flames of fire. As long as the sun shines and the waters flow, this land will be here to give life to men and animals. We cannot sell the lives of men and animals, therefore we cannot sell this land.

1. Describe the attitudes of native Americans ("Indians") to the land.   3

Source B is about the causes of the Civil War.

Source B

> A bitter civil war was fought between 1861 and 1865. On one side was the slave-owning South, the Confederate states. They were fighting for the right to manage their own affairs and to opt out of the Union if they wished. On the other side were the Northern states, generally opposed to slavery and determined that America should stay together in one Union.

2. Explain why slavery was a cause of the Civil War.   3

Marks

SECTION B: ENQUIRY SKILLS

The following sources are about the activities of the Ku Klux Klan.

Study the sources carefully and answer the questions which follow.

You should use your own knowledge where appropriate.

Source C is a cartoon from a newspaper published in the north of America in 1873.

Source C

WHITE TERRORISM

3. How useful is **Source C** as evidence of the activities of the Ku Klux Klan?   **4**

4. How fully does **Source C** show what the Ku Klux Klan was like?

    You should use **your own knowledge** and give reasons for your answer.   **3**

[Turn over

Mark

Source D describes some of the methods used by the Ku Klux Klan.

Source D

> The Ku Klux Klan was a secret society set up to terrorise black people. They dressed in ghostly white costumes and carried burning crosses. The Klan often used violence and did not hesitate at torture, arson and murder. Many blacks were hanged without a proper trial. A favourite target was burning the local school which had been opened to give ex slaves and their children a chance to be educated.

5.   To what extent do **Sources C** and **D** agree about the treatment of black people after the Civil War?   **4**

[END OF CONTEXT IIIA]

Marks

UNIT III—PEOPLE AND POWER

CONTEXT B: INDIA 1917–1947

SECTION A: KNOWLEDGE AND UNDERSTANDING

Study the information in the sources. You must also use your own knowledge in your answers.

Source A describes the importance of India to Britain.

Source A

> India had an important role to play in the British Empire. India exported a variety of goods to Britain and in return she was the largest single market for British imports, especially for cotton goods and heavy engineering.

1. Explain why control of India was good for Britain.   **3**

Source B describes what happened at Amritsar in 1919.

Source B

> In 1919 the British government extended its powers to combat anti-British activities. At Amritsar in the Punjab about 10 000 demonstrators came face to face with British troops in an open space known as the Jallianwalla Bagh which only had one exit. The result was to be known as the Amritsar massacre.

2. Describe the events at Amritsar in April 1919.   **3**

[Turn over

Mark

SECTION B: ENQUIRY SKILLS

The following sources are about Muslim Direct Action.

**Study the sources carefully and answer the questions which follow.
You should use your own knowledge where appropriate.**

Source C is a Muslim League poster from 1946. It shows the areas claimed by Muslims.

Source C

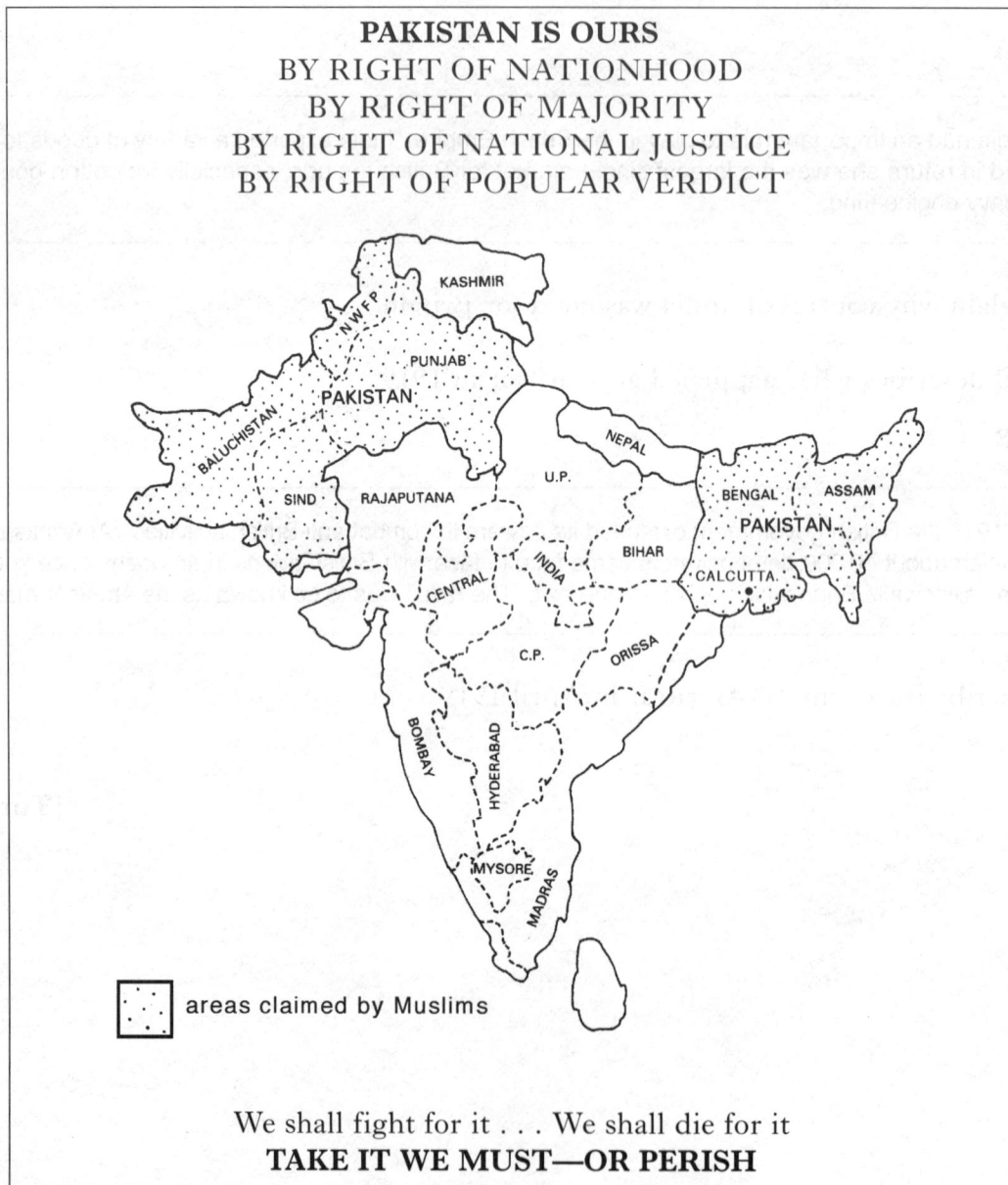

**PAKISTAN IS OURS
BY RIGHT OF NATIONHOOD
BY RIGHT OF MAJORITY
BY RIGHT OF NATIONAL JUSTICE
BY RIGHT OF POPULAR VERDICT**

areas claimed by Muslims

We shall fight for it . . . We shall die for it
TAKE IT WE MUST—OR PERISH

3. How useful is **Source C** as evidence of Muslim attitudes in 1946?   **4**

4. How fully does **Source C** reveal the views about partition of people living in India in 1946?

    You should use **your own knowledge** and give reasons for your answer.   **3**

In **Source D**, an Indian historian describes Muslim Direct Action Day, August 16th, 1946.

Source D

> Speeches made by some of their leaders encouraged Muslims to fight for Pakistan on Direct Action Day. When the day came, Muslims in Calcutta attacked Hindu shopkeepers, kicked or stabbed them, then smashed and looted their shops. The Hindus retaliated, and in forty-eight hours nearly 5000 people were killed.

5. How far do **Sources C** and **D** agree about Muslim Direct Action? 			**4**

[END OF CONTEXT IIIB]

Mark

UNIT III—PEOPLE AND POWER

> ### CONTEXT C: RUSSIA 1914–1941

SECTION A: KNOWLEDGE AND UNDERSTANDING

Study the information in the sources. You must also use your own knowledge in your answers.

Source A is about the power of the Russian Tsars.

Source A

> The ruler of Russia was called the Tsar. It was a hereditary title. This meant that when the Tsar died, the crown went to his eldest son. He was chief of the armed forces and head of the Russian Orthodox Church. People obeyed him not just because he was the Tsar but because he had been chosen by God to rule over them.

1. Why were Russian Tsars so powerful?   **3**

Source B is taken from a letter by Lenin to the Central Committee of the Bolshevik Party.

Source B

> The truth about Kolchak and Denikin has now been fully revealed. They are responsible for the shooting of tens of thousands of workers, the flogging of peasants in entire districts, and endless looting. Let every worker know what he is fighting for, and what awaits him in the event of a White victory.

2. Describe the ways Russian civilians suffered during the Civil War.   **3**

Marks

SECTION B: ENQUIRY SKILLS

The following sources are about the New Economic Policy.

Study the sources carefully and answer the questions which follow.
You should use your own knowledge where appropriate.

Source C was produced using official Soviet figures released in the late 1920s.

Source C

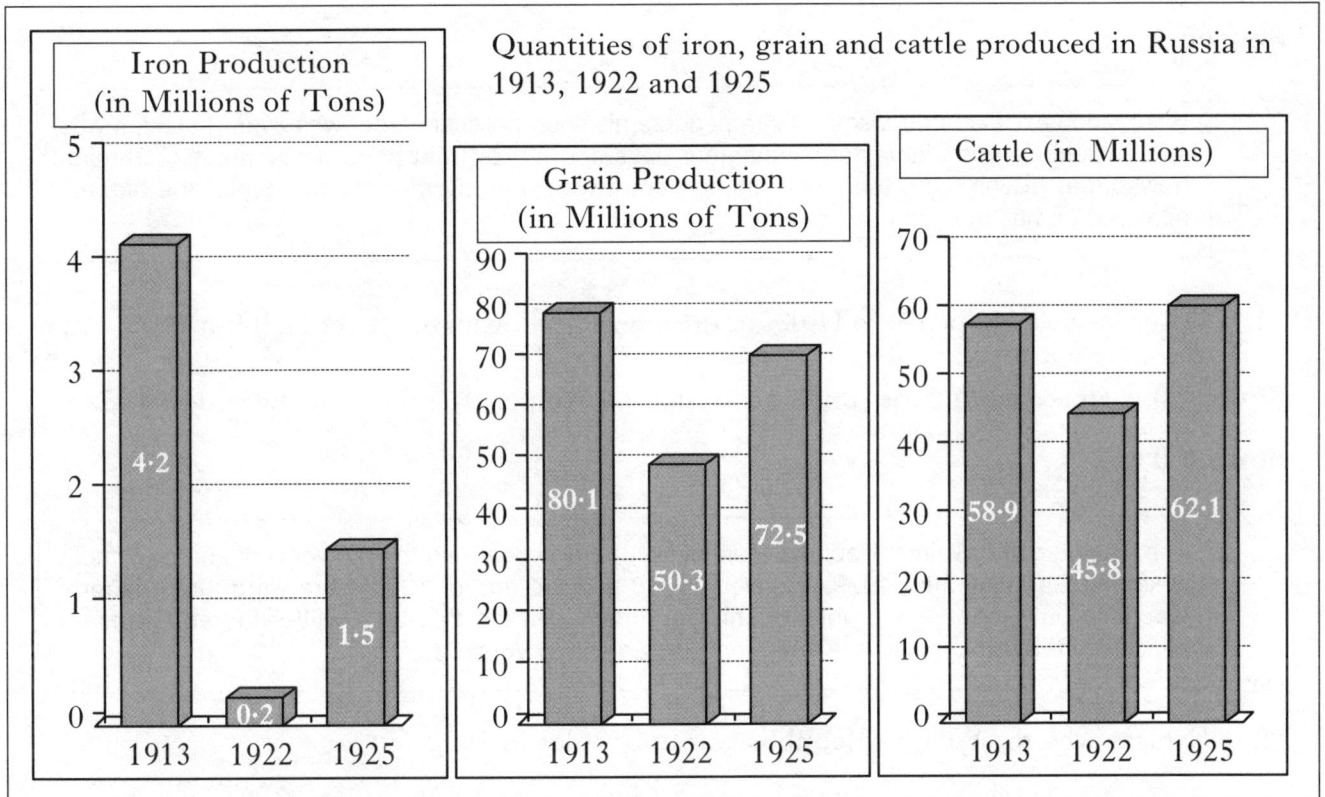

Quantities of iron, grain and cattle produced in Russia in 1913, 1922 and 1925

Iron Production (in Millions of Tons): 1913 = 4·2, 1922 = 0·2, 1925 = 1·5

Grain Production (in Millions of Tons): 1913 = 80·1, 1922 = 50·3, 1925 = 72·5

Cattle (in Millions): 1913 = 58·9, 1922 = 45·8, 1925 = 62·1

3. How useful is **Source C** as evidence of the effects of the New Economic Policy?   4

4. How fully does **Source C** show the successes of the New Economic Policy?

    You should use **your own knowledge** and give reasons for your answer.   3

Source D is from "The Russian Revolution" by the historian, J. Quinn.

Source D

> As soon as the peasants became the real owners of the land, they began to work with an enthusiasm previously unknown. By 1925 grain production had increased and was back to the levels of 1913. Animals, which had been largely wiped out during the war, began to reappear in great numbers. Starvation was reduced and industrial production began to climb again.

5. To what extent do **Sources C** and **D** agree about the effects of the New Economic Policy?   4

[END OF CONTEXT IIIC]

Mark

UNIT III—PEOPLE AND POWER

CONTEXT D: GERMANY 1918–1939

SECTION A: KNOWLEDGE AND UNDERSTANDING

Study the information in the sources. You must also use your own knowledge in your answers.

Source A describes Hitler's trial after the 1923 Beer Hall Putsch in Munich.

Source A

> Hitler stood accused of treason. It seemed that his short political career was over. In fact, it was just beginning. His trial lasted twenty-four days and it was front page news in every German newspaper. Everything that Hitler said in court was read by millions of people, the biggest audience he had ever had.

1. Describe what happened to Hitler in the months following the Beer Hall Putsch of 1923.   **3**

Source B is an account of the problems facing the Weimar Republic by the end of 1932.

Source B

> The leaders of the Weimar Republic found it very hard to deal with the problems of unemployment which hit Germany after 1929. Between 1930 and the end of 1932 there were three general elections but Germany's problems still continued. During this time, Hitler toured Germany attacking the Weimar politicians and promising an end to Versailles.

2. Explain why the Weimar Republic was unpopular in 1932.   **3**

SECTION B: ENQUIRY SKILLS

The following sources are about the Hitler Youth Movement.

Study the sources carefully and answer the questions which follow.
You should use your own knowledge where appropriate.

Source C is from a children's colouring book produced by the Nazis in the mid 1930s.

Source C

HITLER YOUTH AT CAMP

3. How useful is **Source C** as evidence of the popularity of the Hitler Youth in Nazi
    Germany?   4

Source D is from a recent textbook describing some of the activities of the Hitler Youth.

Source D

> Many young people were attracted by the exciting and interesting range of activities of the Youth
> movement. There were many outdoor events such as camping and hiking as well as sports.
> Some enjoyed the military aspects of the Youth movement: the uniforms; the marching and the
> discipline. Other young people liked the music that was a frequent part of their military parades.

4. To what extent do **Sources C** and **D** agree on the appeal of the Hitler Youth movement?   4

5. How fully does **Source D** describe the ways Nazis attracted young people?

    You should use **your own knowledge** and give reasons for your answer   3

[END OF CONTEXT IIID]

[END OF QUESTION PAPER]

[BLANK PAGE]

C

1540/103

SCOTTISH
CERTIFICATE OF
EDUCATION
1999

THURSDAY, 13 MAY
10.50 AM – 12.35 PM

HISTORY
STANDARD GRADE
Credit Level

Answer questions from Unit I **and** Unit II **and** Unit III.

Choose only **one** Context from each Unit and answer Sections A **and** B. The Contexts chosen should be those you have studied.

The Contexts in each Unit are:

Number the questions as shown in the question paper.

Some sources have been adapted or translated.

SCOTTISH
QUALIFICATIONS
AUTHORITY

Marks

UNIT I—CHANGING LIFE IN SCOTLAND AND BRITAIN

CONTEXT A: 1750s–1850s

SECTION A: KNOWLEDGE AND UNDERSTANDING

> Thousands of Highland families left their homelands forever between 1750 and 1850.

1. Why did so many people leave the Highlands and Islands of Scotland between 1750 and 1850?

4

> Many people had high hopes for parliamentary reform in 1832, but were dissatisfied with the results.

2. How important was the Reform Act of 1832 in making Britain more democratic?

4

SECTION B: ENQUIRY SKILLS

The issue for investigating is:

> Overcrowded housing was the main cause of poor health in Scotland between 1800 and 1850.

Study the sources carefully and answer the questions which follow.
You should use your own knowledge where appropriate.

Source A is from a report about Glasgow, written by Dr Robert Graham in 1818.

Source A

> If any man wonders at the reasons for fever among the lower classes in Glasgow, let him take the walk which I did today through an alley, from four to five feet wide, between houses five floors high. We found one lodging house, fifteen feet long by nine feet wide, where fifteen people sometimes lived. Each family was provided with one bed.

Source B is from a report by Dr W. L. Lawrie about conditions in Greenock in 1842.

Source B

> In one part of Market Street is a dunghill which is never removed. Next to it there is a block of houses and in the summer each house swarms with flies. If food and drink are left uncovered for a minute flies attack them.

Marks

Source C is from the Report on the Sanitary Conditions of the Labouring Population of Great Britain, published in 1842.

Source C

> Various diseases are caused by foul air produced by decomposing animal and vegetable matter and by damp, filthy closes and overcrowded dwellings.

3. How useful are **Sources A** and **B** for investigating whether or not overcrowded housing was the main cause of poor health in Scotland, between 1800 and 1850?   **4**

4. What evidence is there in the sources to support the view that overcrowded housing was the main cause of poor health in Scotland, between 1800 and 1850?

    What evidence in the sources suggests that there were other reasons for poor health in Scotland between 1800 and 1850?   **6**

5. How important do you think overcrowded housing was as a cause of poor health in Scotland between 1800 and 1850? You should use evidence from the sources and your own knowledge to come to a balanced conclusion.   **5**

[END OF CONTEXT IA]

Marks

UNIT I—CHANGING LIFE IN SCOTLAND AND BRITAIN

CONTEXT B: 1830s–1930s

SECTION A: KNOWLEDGE AND UNDERSTANDING

> The Irish famine of the 1840s caused mass emigration from Ireland to Britain.

1. What were the effects of Irish immigration on Scotland?   **4**

> In 1911 the Suffragette campaign became more militant.

2. How important was the militant Suffragette campaign in persuading the government to grant the vote to women?

   4

SECTION B: ENQUIRY SKILLS

The issue for investigating is:

> Lack of hygiene was the main reason for the spread of disease in Scotland between 1830 and 1880.

Study the sources carefully and answer the questions which follow.
You should use your own knowledge where appropriate.

Source A is from a report written in 1842 on the Sanitary Conditions of the Labouring Population of Scotland. This extract describes conditions in Stirling.

Source A

> The filth of the prison floats down the public streets and gives off a disgusting smell. The slaughter house is near the top of the town, and the blood from it is allowed to flow down the public streets. There are no public toilets and the common stairs and closes, and even the public streets, are used as toilets.

Source B is an account by Dr Arnott of conditions in Glasgow in 1842.

Source B

> In Glasgow, the great mass of the fever cases occurred in the areas in which the poorest lived. In these dwellings we saw half dressed wretches crowding together to be warm. Although it was the middle of the day, several women were under a blanket, because other women were wearing the only set of clothes.
>
> Who can wonder that disease should spread in such situations!

Source C is from a report about conditions in Greenock in 1842.

Source C

> Most of the dwellings of the poor are in very narrow closes or alleys with little ventilation. The space between the houses is so narrow as to exclude the sun. The houses are generally two or three storeys high, divided into flats with four or five families in each flat. They have one or two rooms each of about eight to ten feet square.

3. How valuable are **Sources A** and **B** for investigating the spread of disease in Scotland between 1830 and 1880?   **4**

4. What evidence in the sources supports the view that lack of hygiene was the main reason for the spread of disease in Scotland between 1830 and 1880?

   What evidence in the sources suggests that lack of hygiene was not the main reason for the spread of disease in Scotland between 1830 and 1880?   **6**

5. How important do you think lack of hygiene was as a cause of the spread of disease in Scotland between 1830 and 1880? You should use evidence from the sources and your own knowledge to reach a balanced conclusion.   **5**

[END OF CONTEXT 1B]

Mark.

UNIT I—CHANGING LIFE IN SCOTLAND AND BRITAIN

CONTEXT C: 1880s–Present Day

SECTION A: KNOWLEDGE AND UNDERSTANDING

Suffragettes stopped their violence and helped with the war effort.

1. How important was women's contribution to the war effort in winning them the vote?   4

Since 1880 there have been changes in the distribution of population in Britain.

2. Explain the changes in the distribution of population in Britain since 1880.   4

SECTION B: ENQUIRY SKILLS

The issue for investigating is:

Housing in Scotland improved greatly between the 1880s and the 1930s.

Study the sources carefully and answer the questions which follow.
You should use your own knowledge where appropriate.

In **Source A** Georgina Robertson describes girls' lodgings in Fraserburgh in 1891.

Source A

Many of the girls' rooms aren't fit for human habitation—smoky, dirty, draughty, without cupboards or shelves and only one bedstead to every three girls. The girls have to live, cook, and wash, as well as sleep, in a very small space. But the most crying evil is the lack of toilets.

In **Source B** Nellie Edgar describes her new council house in Glasgow which she moved into in the 1930s.

Source B

My parents' room was the parlour too, so they had their bed in it and a three piece suite. As well as that, we had a real living room separate from the kitchen, and a bathroom. No more tin tubs, and there was the garden.

Marks

In **Source C** Molly Weir describes her childhood home in Glasgow in the 1930s.

Source C

> We called our room and kitchen a house for we'd never heard of the word "flat" when I was a wee girl. An outside toilet had to be shared with two other families. There were several large families living in a single room. One family had fourteen children and they all lived in one room.

3. How valuable are **Sources A** and **B** for investigating whether or not housing in Scotland improved greatly in the period 1880s–1930s?   **4**

4. What evidence is there in the sources that housing in Scotland improved greatly between the 1880s and 1930s?

   What evidence is there in the sources that housing in Scotland did not improve greatly between the 1880s and the 1930s?   **6**

5. How greatly do you think that housing in Scotland improved between the 1880s and 1930s? You should use evidence from the sources and your own knowledge to reach a balanced conclusion.   **5**

[END OF CONTEXT IC]

Mark

UNIT II—INTERNATIONAL COOPERATION AND CONFLICT

CONTEXT A: 1790s–1820s

SECTION A: KNOWLEDGE AND UNDERSTANDING

No sector of the British population escaped the effects of war.

(Note: for this answer you should write a short essay of several paragraphs.)

1. Describe the hardships faced during the wars with France by

    EITHER

    (*a*) sailors serving in Nelson's navy   **8**

    OR

    (*b*) civilians in Britain   **8**

SECTION B: ENQUIRY SKILLS

The sources below relate to British reactions to the Revolution in France.

**Study the sources carefully and answer the questions which follow.
You should use your own knowledge where appropriate.**

Source A is an account of the reactions of the Edinburgh lawyer Andrew Fletcher to the French Revolution.

Source A

> At this time, 1791 and 1792, the grand principles of the French revolution filled the thoughts and stirred the passions of all thinking and feeling men. Mr Fletcher was an ardent admirer of the first principles of that revolution. He loved liberty, because he firmly believed that a free government was the only means of promoting national improvement and happiness. I believe he would have died for his principles as cheerfully as any martyr.

2. What was the attitude of Andrew Fletcher to the French Revolution as outlined in **Source A**?   4

Source B is a description by the historian David Thompson of the way in which people reacted to news of events in France at the start of the revolution.

Source B

> When the first news of the setting up of the Constituent Assembly in France reached England nearly everyone was pleased. The fall of the Bastille may have worried some people, but to the reformers and to the writers and thinkers who hated the cruelty and injustice of the old system in France, the destruction of the ancient prison was a sign of a new life. Josiah Wedgwood, the pottery manufacturer, welcomed "The wonderful revolution" as the start of a new age. Robert Burns sent enthusiastic greetings to the new Government in France.

3. To what extent does the evidence about British reactions to the French Revolution given in **Source A** agree with that in **Source B**?   4

4. How fully does the evidence in **Sources A** and **B** describe British reactions to the French Revolution? You should use your own knowledge and give reasons for your answer.   5

[END OF CONTEXT IIA]

Mark.

UNIT II—INTERNATIONAL COOPERATION AND CONFLICT

CONTEXT B: 1890s–1920s

SECTION A: KNOWLEDGE AND UNDERSTANDING

The war which began in August 1914 was a new experience in human history.

(Note: for this answer you should write a short essay of several paragraphs.)

1. Describe fully the ways in which the First World War affected the lives of

EITHER

(a) civilians in Britain   **8**

OR

(b) soldiers on the Western Front   **8**

SECTION B: ENQUIRY SKILLS

The sources below relate to the rivalry between Britain and Germany before the First World War.

Study the sources carefully and answer the questions which follow.
You should use your own knowledge where appropriate.

Source A was written by the British Foreign Secretary in 1911.

Source A

> The worry among the British public about Germany comes entirely from the question of German naval expenditure. This is very considerable and may be increased. If it is increased, it will show the world that Germany's intention is to build a fleet which is bigger than the British fleet. If she had a fleet bigger than the British fleet she could blockade our trade, defeat us at sea and be in London in a very short time with her army.

2. What was the attitude of the British public towards the growth of the German navy according to **Source A**?   4

Source B was written by a journalist the day before Britain declared war on Germany.

Source B

> Germany has always been disliked and distrusted for her bullying sabre rattling, the mailed fist and the spiked helmet. These are symbols of violence and brute force. Indeed she has been suspected for years of looking forward to a war with Great Britain.

3. How far do **Sources A** and **B** agree that Germany was a threat to Britain before 1914?   4

4. How fully do **Sources A** and **B** explain the worsening relations between Britain and Germany? You should use your own knowledge and give reasons for your answer.   5

[END OF CONTEXT IIB]

Mark

UNIT II—INTERNATIONAL COOPERATION AND CONFLICT

CONTEXT C: 1930s–1960s

SECTION A: KNOWLEDGE AND UNDERSTANDING

During the Second World War civilians were in the front line of attack.

(Note: for this answer you should write a short essay of several paragraphs.)

1. Describe fully civilian life during the Second World War in

   EITHER

   (*a*) Britain   **8**

   OR

   (*b*) Germany   **8**

Page twelve

Marks

SECTION B: ENQUIRY SKILLS

The following sources give evidence about tensions in Europe before the Second World War.

**Study the sources carefully and answer the questions which follow.
You should use your own knowledge where appropriate.**

Source A is a British cartoon, published in the spring of 1938.

Source A

"Why should we take a stand about someone pushing someone else when it's all so far away..?"

INCREASING PRESSURE

2.   What is the attitude of **Source A** towards events in Europe in early 1938?   **4**

Source B is from an article written about the Munich Agreement by Clement Attlee and printed in "The Daily Herald" in September 1938.

Source B

> Another humiliating surrender has been made to violence. Hitler has been made master of Europe and the danger of another war has not been averted. This is called a peaceful settlement. It is nothing of the kind. Terms of surrender have been forced on the Czechs by Britain and France who have acted not from any considerations of justice but under threat of war from Germany.

3.   To what extent do **Sources A** and **B** agree about events in Europe in 1938?   **4**

4.   How fully do **Sources A** and **B** describe British reactions to events in Europe in 1938?
     You should use your own knowledge and give reasons for your answer.   **5**

[END OF CONTEXT IIC]

Mark.

UNIT III—PEOPLE AND POWER

> ### CONTEXT A: USA 1850–1880

SECTION A: KNOWLEDGE AND UNDERSTANDING

> Some Northern immigrants were insultingly called "carpet-baggers".

1. Describe briefly the activities of carpet-baggers in the South after the war.   **3**

> A secret society, the Ku Klux Klan, terrorised the Negroes and the Whites who directed them.

2. Explain why the Ku Klux Klan carried out their activities.   **5**

SECTION B: ENQUIRY SKILLS

The sources below are about attitudes to slavery as a cause of the American Civil War.

**Study the sources carefully and answer the questions which follow.
You should use your own knowledge where appropriate.**

Source A is from "Abraham Lincoln" by Norman Kolpas.

Source A

> Lincoln addressed the South directly in saying that although the Republicans thought slavery was wrong, they would not risk destroying the Union by trying to stamp it out. However, he stressed that he would not stand for the spread of Southern slavery into any new territories, saying: "Thinking slavery wrong, as we do, we cannot yield to slave-owners."

3. What was Lincoln's attitude to slavery, according to **Source A**?   **4**

Marks

Source B is from a speech by John C. Calhoun in the US Senate before the Civil War.

Source B

> We of the South cannot surrender our way of life. To keep things the way they are between the two races living in the South is essential to the peace and happiness of both. Slavery is so much part of our society that to destroy it would be to destroy us as a people. I believe that the existing relations between the two races in the slave-holding states is a good thing. Never before has the black race been so civilised and so improved.

4. To what extent does **Source B** disagree with **Source A** about slavery?   **4**

[END OF CONTEXT IIIA]

UNIT III—PEOPLE AND POWER

CONTEXT B: INDIA 1917–1947

SECTION A: KNOWLEDGE AND UNDERSTANDING

> "We command, you obey", said the British, "for we know what is good for you."

1. What methods of British rule caused problems in India?   3

> In 1947 Partition tore communities apart.

2. Explain why the Partition of India caused problems.   5

SECTION B: ENQUIRY SKILLS

The sources below give evidence about Muslim Direct Action.

**Study the sources carefully and answer the questions which follow.
You should use your own knowledge where appropriate.**

Source A is from a speech by Muhammad Ali Jinnah on August 16, 1946.

Source A

> What we have done today is the most historic act in our history. In the Muslim League we have never done anything to achieve our aim of creating Pakistan except by legal, constitutional methods. Our efforts have been hindered at every turn. Now we are forced into this limited, controlled aggression. This day we bid goodbye to constitutional methods. This has been a day of Direct Action.

3. What was the attitude of the author towards Direct Action Day?   4

Source B is from "The Partition of India" by V. P. Kanitkar.

Source B

> On August 16th, 1946, small groups of hired thugs, called goondas, crossed the river into the city of Calcutta. They were armed with bamboo sticks, iron bars, bottles and knives. Muhammad Ali Jinnah had announced that this was to be Direct Action Day when Muslims would reaffirm their desire to have their own separate country. It was prearranged violence. Hindus were stabbed and beaten and their shops looted. In forty eight hours over 5000 died.

4.   To what extent do **Sources A** and **B** agree about Direct Action Day?   4

[END OF CONTEXT IIIB]

Marks

UNIT III—PEOPLE AND POWER

CONTEXT C: RUSSIA 1914–1941

SECTION A: KNOWLEDGE AND UNDERSTANDING

> By the winter of 1916–1917 there was a serious government crisis in Russia.

1. Why did opposition to the Tsar grow until he was overthrown in March 1917?   5

> By 1917 the Russian armies were in low spirits following the failure of their 1916 offensive.

2. What were some of the problems which the Russian armies faced by early 1917?   3

SECTION B: ENQUIRY SKILLS

The sources below relate to the Civil War in Russia between 1918 and 1921.

**Study the sources carefully and answer the questions which follow.
You should use your own knowledge where appropriate.**

Source A is from a leaflet distributed by the Bolsheviks to Allied troops invading Russia in 1919.

Source A

> For the first time in history the working people have control of their country. The workers of all countries are striving to achieve this. We in Russia have succeeded. We have thrown off the rule of the Tsar, of landlords and of capitalists. But we still have tremendous difficulties to overcome. We cannot build a new society in a day. We deserve to be left alone. We ask you, are you going to crush us? To help give Russia back to the landlords, the capitalists and the Tsar?

3. What is the attitude shown in **Source A** towards the situation in Russia in 1919?   4

Marks

Source B is part of a speech by Winston Churchill in 1919 on Allied interference in Russia during the Civil War.

Source B

> Everyone knows why the Allied Armies were sent there. They were sent as part of our operation against Germany. It was vitally necessary to take every measure in regard to Russia during the war which would keep as many German troops as possible on the Russian front, and prevent the movement of German armies of more than a million men to the Western Front. That was the reason why we gave aid in minor ways to the white armies of Admiral Kolchak and General Denikin.

4. To what extent do **Sources A** and **B** agree about Allied intervention in the Russian Civil War?   **4**

[END OF CONTEXT IIIC]

Mark.

UNIT III—PEOPLE AND POWER

CONTEXT D: GERMANY 1918–1939

SECTION A: KNOWLEDGE AND UNDERSTANDING

Hitler and the Nazi party believed young people were very important.

---

1. Give a brief account of the methods used by the Nazis to control young people in Germany.

   3

The chances of any effective opposition to Nazi rule were small.

---

2. Why was there so little opposition to the Nazi government?

   5

SECTION B: ENQUIRY SKILLS

The sources below give evidence about the Nazi rise to power in Germany.

Study the sources carefully and answer the questions which follow.
You should use your own knowledge where appropriate.

Source A comes from a book written by Albert Speer, who joined the Nazi party in 1931 and became an important member of Hitler's government.

Source A

There was hope and new ideas. The dangers of communism could be stopped and, instead of hopeless unemployment, Germany could move towards economic recovery. My mother saw an SA parade in the street. The sight of such discipline in a time of chaos, the impression of energy in a time of hopelessness, seems to have won her over.

---

3. Discuss the attitude towards the Nazi party shown in **Source A**.

   4

Marks

Source B was written in 1940 by Neville Henderson, who had been British ambassador to Germany before the war.

Source B

> The Germans are an easily persuaded and disciplined people who like being governed. The young people of Germany were enthusiastic over a movement which appealed so strongly to the young. The German is perfectly happy when he is wearing a uniform, marching in step and singing in chorus.

4.   To what extent do **Sources A** and **B** agree about the appeal of the Nazi party?   **4**

[END OF CONTEXT IIID]

[END OF QUESTION PAPER]

[BLANK PAGE]

[BLANK PAGE]

[BLANK PAGE]

C

1540/403

NATIONAL
QUALIFICATIONS
2000

TUESDAY, 6 JUNE
10.50 AM – 12.35 PM

HISTORY
STANDARD GRADE
Credit Level

Answer questions from Unit I **and** Unit II **and** Unit III.

Choose only **one** Context from each Unit and answer Sections A **and** B. The Contexts chosen should be those you have studied.

The Contexts in each Unit are:

Number the questions as shown in the question paper.

Some sources have been adapted or translated.

SCOTTISH
QUALIFICATIONS
AUTHORITY

Marks

UNIT I—CHANGING LIFE IN SCOTLAND AND BRITAIN

CONTEXT A: 1750s–1850s

SECTION A: KNOWLEDGE AND UNDERSTANDING

Improved medical knowledge contributed towards a decrease in the death rate.

1. To what extent did improved medical knowledge cause the population to increase during the period 1750–1850?   5

The coming of the mill caused huge changes in working conditions.

2. Describe the changes in working conditions brought about by the coming of textile factories.   3

SECTION B: ENQUIRY SKILLS

The issue for investigating is:

Technological changes during the period 1750–1850 improved the lives of Scottish farmers.

Study the sources carefully and answer the questions which follow.
You should use your own knowledge where appropriate.

Source A is from Thomas Somerville's autobiography, "My Own Life and Times, 1741–1814".

Source A

Scottish farmers were unwilling to run the risk of experiments or to depart from the ancient, inefficient methods of farming. A few enlightened gentlemen who farmed their own estates began agricultural improvements and introduced new, improved ploughs and methods of drainage. They were followed by a number of tenants who obtained long leases. Some made so much money by the new farming that they were able to purchase estates.

Marks

Source B is from "Farming and the Countryside, 1700–1900" by modern historians, Eric Simpson and Nicholas Tate.

Source B

> Eventually, tenant farmers as well as lairds took the lead in introducing the new, labour-saving techniques. The Old Scots Plough was gradually replaced by the lighter chain-plough. Scythes and later reapers came to replace the sickle on many farms. Through these methods and others the growing population was fed.

Source C is from "A Tour Through Scotland in 1792–1794" by John Lettice.

Source C

> The present farmer has, as a result of improved farming methods on his estate, evicted eight dependent cottagers who from father to son had managed to maintain themselves comfortably and brought up their children with decency. These cottagers, being turned adrift, have had to send their children to work in factories.

3. How useful are **Sources A** and **B** for investigating the effects of new technology in Scottish farming in the period 1750–1850?   4

4. What evidence is there in the sources to support the view that technological changes during the period 1750–1850 improved the lives of Scottish farmers?

   What evidence is there in the sources to suggest that technological changes during the period 1750–1850 did **not** improve the lives of Scottish farmers?   6

5. How true is it to say that technological changes during the period 1750–1850 improved the lives of Scottish farmers? You must use **evidence from the sources** and **your own knowledge** to reach a balanced conclusion.   5

[END OF CONTEXT IA]

Marks

UNIT I—CHANGING LIFE IN SCOTLAND AND BRITAIN

CONTEXT B: 1830s–1930s

SECTION A: KNOWLEDGE AND UNDERSTANDING

> Between 1830 and 1900 a rising birth rate led to an increase in population.

1. How important a factor was a rising birth rate in explaining population growth between 1830 and 1930?   **5**

> A few machines can do the work of many hands.

2. Give a brief account of changes in working conditions for farm workers between 1830 and 1930.   **3**

SECTION B: ENQUIRY SKILLS

The issue for investigating is:

> Railways were universally welcomed between 1840 and 1900.

Study the sources carefully and answer the questions which follow.
You should use your own knowledge where appropriate.

Source A is from an article in the Scottish Railway Gazette for April 1845.

Source A

> Railways will mean that all parts of the country will become more opened up. Land in the interior will, by a system of cheap and rapid transport for manure and farm produce, become almost as valuable as land on the coast. The man of business can as easily join his family at a distance of 10 or 12 miles as could formerly be done at 2 or 3 miles.

Marks

In **Source B,** J. McDonald writes in his memoirs about the early days of railways.

Source B

> My stepmother took her place in the train. She had her handkerchief tightly pressed to her eyes so that she might see nothing. A more extreme picture of terror and dejection I never saw. I remember well hearing the criticisms of railways: their dangers, their abilities to injure health, their causing cows to refuse to be milked; their ruin of the horse breeding trade.

Source C was written by the historian R.N. Rundle.

Source C

> With the introduction of cheap workmen's fares, better paid workmen could live in a suburb and travel to work by train. The upper and middle classes moved further into the countryside so villages near cities grew into towns. Holiday resorts were also created by the railway. Factories had no longer to be created on coal fields as coal could be carried cheaply by rail. However, coaching and canal systems were soon both badly affected.

3. How useful are **Sources A** and **B** for investigating whether railways were universally welcomed between 1840 and 1900?   4

4. What evidence in the sources supports the view that railways were universally welcomed?

   What evidence in the sources suggests that railways were **not** universally welcomed?   6

5. To what extent were railways universally welcomed between 1840 and 1900? You must use **evidence from the sources** and **your own knowledge** to reach a balanced conclusion.   5

[END OF CONTEXT 1B]

Mark

UNIT I—CHANGING LIFE IN SCOTLAND AND BRITAIN

> ### CONTEXT C: 1880s–Present Day

SECTION A: KNOWLEDGE AND UNDERSTANDING

> Women's lives changed after the First World War.

1. In what ways did the employment of women change after 1918?   **3**

> The population of Scotland has grown steadily over the last 100 years.

2. Explain the importance of better medical care in causing Scotland's population increase over the last 100 years.   **5**

SECTION B: ENQUIRY SKILLS

The issue for investigating is:

> Motor transport greatly improved people's lives in the 20th century.

Study the sources carefully and answer the questions which follow.
You should use your own knowledge where appropriate.

Source A is from an interview with a person living in a remote glen in the Highlands of Scotland in the 1970s.

Source A

> In the old days everyone had bicycles. Nowadays, you find there are few young people without a motor cycle or a car. Half the time they are people who can't afford it and that has cut down their standard of living. People have become lazy. They never think of cycling anywhere. And for those who don't own cars, if you live off the main bus routes, then the problems are enormous. Local shops have shut down.

Source B was written by historian Richard Tames in 1970 and describes the development of road transport.

Source B

> The petrol driven vehicle offered many advantages. It could go almost anywhere. The manufacturer and shopkeeper with deliveries to make saw obvious advantages in the door-to-door service and freedom from railway timetables. Motor transport was often cheaper, as road haulage companies were able to offer special rates.

Source C is from "The Pendulum Years" by B. Levin.

Source C

> Container lorries revolutionised the entire pattern of shifting goods and therefore provided a better standard of living for all. However, every lorry added to the burden of impossibly overcrowded roads and contributed its poison to the atmosphere.

3. How useful are **Sources A** and **B** for investigating the effects of motor transport on people's lives in the 20th century?   **4**

4. What evidence is there in the sources to support the view that motor transport greatly improved people's lives in the 20th century?

    What evidence is there in the sources that motor transport has **not** improved people's lives in the 20th century?   **6**

5. Did motor transport greatly improve people's lives in the 20th century? You must use **evidence from the sources** and **your own knowledge** to reach a balanced conclusion.   **5**

[END OF CONTEXT IC]

Marks

UNIT II—INTERNATIONAL COOPERATION AND CONFLICT

CONTEXT A: 1790s–1820s

SECTION A: KNOWLEDGE AND UNDERSTANDING

> Public opinion hardened against France and the danger of war increased.

1. How important a factor was French aggression in causing the war between Britain and France in 1793?   **4**

> In 1815 the Allies agreed on the treatment of France.

2. Explain the reasons for the treatment of France at the Congress of Vienna.   **4**

SECTION B: ENQUIRY SKILLS

The following sources are about life in the British navy, 1797–1798.

**Study the sources carefully and answer the questions which follow.
You should use your own knowledge where appropriate.**

Source A is a sketch entitled "Firing a Cannon on Board a British Warship". It was drawn during the wars against France.

Source A

3. How useful is **Source A** as evidence about conditions in the British navy?   **4**

Marks

Source B is from "Naval Songs and Ballads" by John Mansfield, published in 1903.

Source B

> It is evident from many ballads that there was considerable discontent in the navy. This showed itself in the mutinies of 1797. One common complaint was the bad provisions and cheating by the purser. Another was the difficulty a sailor had in getting paid. A third complaint was the severity of discipline. A pamphlet explains "Almost every petty officer, even of just a month's standing flourishes his stick over the head of the ablest seaman and acts the tyrant over them."

4. What did sailors think about life in the British navy? **5**

In **Source C** a modern historian describes the demands made by Richard Parker during the mutiny at the Nore in 1797.

Source C

> Parker demanded that the Admiralty allow shore leave. He made further points about better pay and then produced two new demands: that more equal distribution be made of prize money to the crew and that the very severe discipline should be made less harsh.

5. How far do **Sources B** and **C** agree about the reasons for discontent in the navy? **4**

[END OF CONTEXT IIA]

Marks

UNIT II—INTERNATIONAL COOPERATION AND CONFLICT

CONTEXT B: 1890s–1920s

SECTION A: KNOWLEDGE AND UNDERSTANDING

> The next major war, Bismarck predicted, would be sparked off by "some damned foolish thing in the Balkans".

1. Assess the importance of the assassinations at Sarajevo in 1914 in starting a war in Europe.   4

> The Treaty of Versailles did not totally please anyone—neither the victors nor the vanquished.

2. For what reasons did countries have their doubts about the Treaty of Versailles?   4

SECTION B: ENQUIRY SKILLS

The following sources are about trench warfare.

**Study the sources carefully and answer the questions which follow.
You should use your own knowledge where appropriate.**

Source A is a photograph taken in 1917 on the Western Front.

Source A

3. How useful is **Source A** as evidence of the conditions in which men fought in the First World War?   4

Marks

Source B was taken from the diary of Private Ernest Atkins who fought on the Western Front in 1917.

Source B

> Not a tree, not a blade of grass: just one vast stretch of poisoned mud and water-filled shell-holes through which men trudge on their constant labours. No one can imagine such a place unless they have actually seen it. The effect on me is worse than shelling or fighting, although there is that as well. Willpower alone keeps me going. Once you lose that, you are finished.

4. How far do **Sources A** and **B** agree about conditions on the Western Front?   4

Source C was written by a soldier who was involved in a battle on the Western Front in 1916.

Source C

> We struggled on through the dreadful mud and the rain. Then came a terrific crack above my head and I felt a jolt in my left shoulder. I watched in an amazed, detached sort of way as my right arm twisted upwards and then hung limp.
>
> I realised that I had been hit. Suddenly I was filled with happiness that I was saved from death and that I would be sent to hospital for treatment. I quickly forgot that I had just taken part in a failure and that I had done nothing to win the war.

5. Discuss the author's attitude towards fighting on the Western Front.   5

[END OF CONTEXT IIB]

UNIT II—INTERNATIONAL COOPERATION AND CONFLICT

CONTEXT C: 1930s–1960s

SECTION A: KNOWLEDGE AND UNDERSTANDING

> When the German army invaded Poland on 1st September 1939, the Second World War began.

1. How important a factor was the German invasion of Poland in causing the Second World War?   **4**

> In 1948 the Cold War nearly became a "hot war"; the cause—Berlin.

2. Explain why Berlin became a crisis point in East–West relations during 1948–1949.   **4**

SECTION B: ENQUIRY SKILLS

The following sources are about the effects of air warfare.

**Study the sources carefully and answer the questions which follow.
You should use your own knowledge where appropriate.**

Source A is a cartoon from the "Daily Record" during the Second World War. It shows Hitler speaking to Goering during a bombing raid.

Source A

*A Taste Of
Their Own
Medicine*

Marks

3. How useful is **Source A** as evidence of the effects of the Allied bombing campaign?   4

In **Source B** a modern historian assesses the effects of the Allied bombing of Germany.

Source B

> In Berlin the damage was severe enough to cause many to leave the city and to close all the schools but less than half of the city's industries stopped work and many of the stoppages were brief. Morale did not break in Berlin or Hamburg. However the bombing helped to make the British people think they were getting a little of their own back on the enemy.

4. To what extent do **Sources A** and **B** agree about the Allied bombing campaign?   4

In **Source C** Nancy Richmond remembers a German air raid over London during the Second World War.

Source C

> The minute the siren went, all the Air Raid Precautions you had read were forgotten and fear took over in the mad dash to the Anderson; the anxious fitting of gas masks and the waiting for the hated drone of the German bombers. I tried to appear calm—mainly for the children's sake. However, inside, I was churning. I had heard of other streets completely "blitzed out". Would we be next?

5. Discuss the attitudes of the author in **Source C** towards an air raid.   5

[END OF CONTEXT IIC]

Mark.

UNIT III—PEOPLE AND POWER

CONTEXT A: USA 1850–1880

SECTION A: KNOWLEDGE AND UNDERSTANDING

> At the end of the Civil War, life for both white and black people in the Southern states was not easy.

(Note: for this answer you should write a short essay of several paragraphs.)

1. Describe fully the problems and difficulties which existed in the South during Reconstruction between 1865 and 1878 for

EITHER

    (*a*) the white population   **8**

OR

    (*b*) the freed slaves   **8**

SECTION B: ENQUIRY SKILLS

The following sources give evidence about slavery as a cause of the American Civil War.

Study the sources carefully and answer the questions which follow.
You should use your own knowledge where appropriate.

Source A was written in 1861 by Orville Browning, a Republican friend of Abraham Lincoln.

Source A

> I believe that slavery is the sole, original cause of the present unhappy condition of affairs. A large majority of the people in the free states of this Union believe as I do; and many of them, good and patriotic people, are anxious that the war shall be made the occasion of wiping slavery out. Our new President will fulfil that aim.

2. How fully does **Source A** explain why Civil War broke out in America in 1861? You should use your own knowledge and give reasons for your answer.   **4**

Marks

Source B was written by historian E. Smith in 1967.

Source B

> Among the causes of the war was the fact that Southerners convinced themselves that the election of Lincoln would be both an insult and a clear danger. Republican-appointed officials would spread abolition propaganda and enforce restrictions against the slave-trade. Above all, slavery would be contained and a President dedicated to the notion that slavery was a moral evil would sit in the White House.

3. To what extent do **Sources A** and **B** agree about the causes of the American Civil War?

4

[END OF CONTEXT IIIA]

Marks

UNIT III—PEOPLE AND POWER

CONTEXT B: INDIA 1917–1947

SECTION A: KNOWLEDGE AND UNDERSTANDING

> Direct British rule of India lasted for only ninety years.

(Note: for this answer you should write a short essay of several paragraphs.)

1. Describe how the British Raj affected the lives of

EITHER

(a) the British in India   **8**

OR

(b) the Indian population   **8**

SECTION B: ENQUIRY SKILLS

The following sources are about religious divisions in India.

**Study the sources carefully and answer the questions which follow.
You should use your own knowledge where appropriate.**

Source A is a Muslim poster from August 16th, 1946.

Source A

> **TODAY** IS
> # DIRECT ACTION DAY
> **TODAY** MUSLIMS OF INDIA DEDICATE ANEW THEIR LIVES AND ALL THEY POSSESS TO THE CAUSE OF FREEDOM
> **TODAY** *LET EVERY MUSLIM SWEAR IN THE NAME OF ALLAH TO RESIST AGGRESSION*
> DIRECT ACTION IS NOW THEIR ONLY COURSE
> *BECAUSE* . . .
> *   *They offered Peace but Peace was spurned*
> *   *They honoured their word but were betrayed*
> *   *They claimed Liberty but are offered Slavery*
> **NOW MIGHT ALONE CAN SECURE THEIR RIGHT**

2. Why was **Source A** produced? You should use your own knowledge and give reasons for your answer.   **4**

Marks

In **Source B** Robert Payne describes Gandhi's hopes for India.

Source B

> All his life Gandhi had dreamed of an India at peace, bringing peace to the world. He also wanted to bring into existence a new India free of foreign domination and dedicated to non-violence. Muslims and Hindus would live quietly side by side. Now, at the very moment when freedom was being taken from the British, the dream of a peaceful India was shattered.

3. Compare the attitudes to the winning of freedom for India in **Sources A** and **B**.   4

[END OF CONTEXT IIIB]

Marks

UNIT III—PEOPLE AND POWER

CONTEXT C: RUSSIA 1914–1941

SECTION A: KNOWLEDGE AND UNDERSTANDING

> When the Bolsheviks seized power in October 1917, they found a country on the verge of economic collapse.

(Note: for this answer you should write a short essay of several paragraphs.)

1. Describe fully the Bolshevik Government's actions and their effects during the period of

EITHER

(*a*) War Communism   **8**

OR

(*b*) the New Economic Policy   **8**

SECTION B: ENQUIRY SKILLS

The following sources are about morale in the Russian army in early 1917.

**Study the sources carefully and answer the questions which follow.
You should use your own knowledge where appropriate.**

Source A is taken from "The End of the Russian Empire" by M. Florinsky.

Source A

> At the beginning of January 1917, General Krimov arrived from the front and asked to be given an opportunity to inform the members of the Duma about the disastrous conditions at the front and the spirit of the army. He said: "There can be no hope of victory until the Government has changed its course to one the army could trust. The spirit of the army is such that the news of the overthrow of the Government would be welcomed with joy. A revolution is coming soon."

2. How fully does **Source A** explain discontent within the Russian army by early 1917?
    You should use your own knowledge and give reasons for your answer.   **4**

Marks

Source B is taken from the January 1917 entry in the diary of a Russian general.

Source B

> The army chaplain complains of the difficulty of his present position. The men, who read many newspapers, are continually asking for explanations and criticising the Government. This is a sad departure but probably inevitable today with the freedom of the press, statements from the Duma and the Rasputin scandal.

3. How far do **Sources A** and **B** agree on discontent in the Russian army?   **4**

[END OF CONTEXT IIIC]

Marks

UNIT III—PEOPLE AND POWER

CONTEXT D: GERMANY 1918–1939

SECTION A: KNOWLEDGE AND UNDERSTANDING

> Once in power, Hitler was able to keep complete control in Germany.

(Note: for this answer you should write a short essay of several paragraphs.)

1. Describe fully Nazi policies between 1933 and 1939 towards

    EITHER

    (*a*) the Jews   **8**

    OR

    (*b*) young people   **8**

SECTION B: ENQUIRY SKILLS

The following sources are about discontent under the Weimar Republic.

**Study the sources carefully and answer the questions which follow.
You should use your own knowledge where appropriate.**

In **Source A** a modern historian describes the impact of the depression.

Source A

> By 1932 nearly one in three of all German workers was unemployed. The Weimar politicians seemed to have no answers to the crisis. As the dole queues lengthened, more and more discontented voters turned to political parties which rejected the Weimar Republic and offered their own brands of dictatorship. The rise in support for the Nazis was even more spectacular than that for the Communists.

2. How fully does the evidence in **Source A** explain reasons for discontent under the Weimar Republic? You should use your own knowledge and give reasons for your answer.   **4**

Marks

In **Source B** a member of the German government comments on the results of the July 1932 election.

Source B

> The discontented German nation is hurrying towards dictatorship. The Nazis have made huge gains. The Communists have also picked up support almost everywhere. More than half the German people have declared themselves against the present state of affairs which exists with the Weimar politicians.

3. How far do **Sources A** and **B** agree about attitudes towards the Weimar Republic?   **4**

[END OF CONTEXT IIID]

[END OF QUESTION PAPER]

[BLANK PAGE]

[BLANK PAGE]

[BLANK PAGE]

1540/403

NATIONAL QUALIFICATIONS 2001	WEDNESDAY, 30 MAY 10.50 AM – 12.35 PM	**HISTORY** STANDARD GRADE Credit Level

Answer questions from Unit I **and** Unit II **and** Unit III.

Choose only **one** Context from each Unit and answer Sections A **and** B. The Contexts chosen should be those you have studied.

The Contexts in each Unit are:

Number the questions as shown in the question paper.

Some sources have been adapted or translated.

SCOTTISH QUALIFICATIONS AUTHORITY

Marks

UNIT I—CHANGING LIFE IN SCOTLAND AND BRITAIN

> ### CONTEXT A: 1750s–1850s

SECTION A: KNOWLEDGE AND UNDERSTANDING

> The growth of the cotton industry was made possible by a technological revolution.

1. Describe the new technology which made possible the mass production of cotton.   **4**

> In Scotland's industrial towns the solution to overcrowding was to build tall tenement buildings.

2. Do you agree that Scotland's urban housing problems were solved by the building of tenements? Explain your answer.   **4**

SECTION B: ENQUIRY SKILLS

The issue for investigating is:

> Radical action in 1820 was a major factor in the struggle for political reform in Scotland.

Study the sources carefully and answer the questions which follow.
You should use your own knowledge where appropriate.

Source A is from "A History of Scotland" by Professor Rosalind Mitchison, published in 1987.

Source A

> The year 1820 witnessed the pathetic incidents of the Radical War. These included a minor skirmish at Bonnymuir which ended in some casualties and three executions. The alarm these events caused left the authorities looking rather foolish. The newspapers pressed home the situation and the discussions which followed were influential in changing Scotland's political situation.

Marks

Source B is from the speech made by the Radical, James Wilson, at his trial in Glasgow in 1820.

Source B

> For my part (in Radical activities) you may condemn me to hanging and mutilation but you cannot destroy what I stand for. I am a pioneer in the forefront of freedom's battles. I have attempted to free my country from political shame and weakness. My conscience tells me that I have only done my duty. Your brief authority will soon cease but my actions will be recorded in history.

Source C is from "A History of the Scottish People" by T. C. Smout.

Source C

> One group of marchers fled after a short fight at Bonnymuir in which four Radicals were wounded. Out of all the number of Radical prisoners taken in 1820, only three were executed—one of them, James Wilson, a weaver, on scandalously slender grounds. Some were transported but most of the remainder were released largely because of the reluctance of juries to find anyone guilty. On the coming of better conditions for working men, agitation decreased throughout the country.

3. How useful are **Sources A** and **B** for investigating whether Radical action was a major factor in the struggle for political reform in Scotland?   4

4. What evidence is there in the sources to support the view that Radical action was a major factor in the struggle for political reform in Scotland?

   What evidence in the sources suggests that Radical action was **not** a major factor in the struggle for political reform in Scotland?   6

5. How important was Radical action in 1820 in the struggle for political reform in Scotland?

   You must use **evidence from the sources** and **your own knowledge** to reach a balanced conclusion.   5

[END OF CONTEXT IA]

Mark.

UNIT I—CHANGING LIFE IN SCOTLAND AND BRITAIN

CONTEXT B: 1830s–1930s

SECTION A: KNOWLEDGE AND UNDERSTANDING

The work in the mines was not as physical as it had been in 1830.

1. Describe the improvements in coal mining brought about by new technology up to 1930.   **4**

In most towns business people put up cheap housing to rent to working people.

2. Explain why there was so much poor housing in towns and cities in the nineteenth century.   **4**

SECTION B: ENQUIRY SKILLS

The issue for investigating is:

The actions of Suffragettes harmed the cause of votes for women.

**Study the sources carefully and answer the questions which follow.
You should use your own knowledge where appropriate.**

Source A is part of a speech made by Dr Marion Gilchrist, a leading Suffragette. She was speaking in 1908 at the opening of the new WSPU headquarters in Glasgow.

Source A

At one time I thought it a great pity that the militant Suffragettes should create rows at Westminster. Now I have been brought round to another view. Nothing has done more for the cause of female suffrage than the militant Suffragettes. They have brought the question to the attention of the public and that is more than those who have carried on quietly for 60 years have achieved.

Marks

Source B is an extract from "Social Change in Scotland" by historian, Richard Dargie, published in 1999.

Source B

> The Suffragettes believed their extreme actions would force the government to give in to their demands. However, their law-breaking seemed to strengthen the argument that women could not be trusted with the vote. The Government took a tough line and the Suffrage movement split over whether it harmed or helped the cause.

Source C is an extract from "Women's Suffrage" written by Mrs Millicent Fawcett in 1912.

Source C

> The Women's Social and Political Union had not attracted any public notice until 1905. By adopting new and startling methods they succeeded in drawing a large amount of public attention to the cause of votes for women. However, many campaigners viewed these methods with disgust. They believed that lawful, peaceful action would prove more effective in the long run as a way of converting the public and the Government to believe in women's suffrage.

3. How useful are **Sources A** and **B** for investigating whether or not the actions of Suffragettes harmed the cause of votes for women?   **4**

4. What evidence is there in the sources that the Suffragettes did harm the cause of votes for women?

   What evidence is there in the sources that the Suffragettes did **not** harm the cause of votes for women?   **6**

5. How true is it to say that the actions of the Suffragettes harmed the cause of votes for women?

   You must use **evidence from the sources** and **your own knowledge** to reach a balanced conclusion.   **5**

[END OF CONTEXT 1B]

Mark.

UNIT I—CHANGING LIFE IN SCOTLAND AND BRITAIN

| CONTEXT C: 1880s–Present Day |

SECTION A: KNOWLEDGE AND UNDERSTANDING

> Throughout the 1900s there were several changes in the way ships were built.

1. Describe how new technology improved shipbuilding in the twentieth century.   4

> The general condition of housing in the cities was slowly improving.

2. How far do you agree that the condition of housing in Scotland improved after 1945?   4

SECTION B: ENQUIRY SKILLS

The issue for investigating is:

> The actions of Suffragettes harmed the cause of votes for women.

**Study the sources carefully and answer the questions which follow.
You should use your own knowledge where appropriate.**

Source A is part of a speech made by Dr Marion Gilchrist, a leading Suffragette. She was speaking in 1908 at the opening of the new WSPU headquarters in Glasgow.

Source A

> At one time I thought it a great pity that the militant Suffragettes should create rows at Westminster. Now I have been brought round to another view. Nothing has done more for the cause of female suffrage than the militant Suffragettes. They have brought the question to the attention of the public and that is more than those who have carried on quietly for 60 years have achieved.

Marks

Source B is an extract from "Social Change in Scotland" by historian, Richard Dargie, published in 1999.

Source B

> The Suffragettes believed their extreme actions would force the government to give in to their demands. However, their law-breaking seemed to strengthen the argument that women could not be trusted with the vote. The Government took a tough line and the Suffrage movement split over whether it harmed or helped the cause.

Source C is an extract from "Women's Suffrage" written by Mrs Millicent Fawcett in 1912.

Source C

> The Women's Social and Political Union had not attracted any public notice until 1905. By adopting new and startling methods they succeeded in drawing a large amount of public attention to the cause of votes for women. However, many campaigners viewed these methods with disgust. They believed that lawful, peaceful action would prove more effective in the long run as a way of converting the public and the Government to believe in women's suffrage.

3. How useful are **Sources A** and **B** for investigating whether or not the actions of Suffragettes harmed the cause of votes for women?   4

4. What evidence is there in the sources that the Suffragettes did harm the cause of votes for women?

    What evidence is there in the sources that the Suffragettes did **not** harm the cause of votes for women?   6

5. How true is it to say that the actions of the Suffragettes harmed the cause of votes for women?

    You must use **evidence from the sources** and **your own knowledge** to reach a balanced conclusion.   5

[END OF CONTEXT IC]

Mark.

UNIT II—INTERNATIONAL COOPERATION AND CONFLICT

CONTEXT A: 1790s–1820s

SECTION A: KNOWLEDGE AND UNDERSTANDING

> In the autumn of 1792 other events occurred which hastened the war.

(Note: for this answer you should write a short essay of several paragraphs.)

1. How important in causing the outbreak of war between France and other European states between 1792 and 1793 was

   EITHER

   (*a*) the fear of Revolution?   **8**

   OR

   (*b*) aggressive French foreign policy?   **8**

SECTION B: ENQUIRY SKILLS

The following sources are about British attitudes to the French Revolution.

**Study the sources carefully and answer the questions which follow.
You should use your own knowledge where appropriate.**

Source A is part of a report which appeared in a Scottish newspaper, the Caledonian Mercury, in September 1790.

Source A

> In France, the triumph of liberty and reason over despotism is an interesting event. That some disturbances and even acts of violence should accompany this great Revolution is in no way surprising; that these have not been more numerous is surprising to every politician. Our hopes in Britain are that the French example will be universally followed, and that the flame they have kindled will consume the remains of despotism in Europe.

2. Discuss the attitude of the author in **Source A** to the French Revolution.   **4**

Source B is from "British Social and Economic History" by historian, C. P. Hill.

Source B

> The French Revolution of 1789 had at first been universally welcomed by many Englishmen of all classes who saw it as a great move towards freedom. This attitude soon changed. The growth of violence and the intention of the leaders of the Revolution to thrust their ideas upon other people swung the ruling classes in Britain against the Revolution.

3.   How fully do **Sources A** and **B** show the reaction in Britain towards events in France?

   You must use **your own knowledge** and give reasons for your answer.   **5**

[END OF CONTEXT IIA]

Mark.

UNIT II—INTERNATIONAL COOPERATION AND CONFLICT

> CONTEXT B: 1890s–1920s

SECTION A: KNOWLEDGE AND UNDERSTANDING

> Alliances and military and naval rivalry hastened the outbreak of war in 1914.

(Note: for this answer you should write a short essay of several paragraphs.)

1. How important as a cause of the First World War was

EITHER

(*a*) the Alliance System?   **8**

OR

(*b*) the Naval Arms Race?   **8**

SECTION B: ENQUIRY SKILLS

The following sources are about British attitudes to the use of poison gas in the First World War.

Study the sources carefully and answer the questions which follow.
You should use your own knowledge where appropriate.

In **Source A** Sir Arthur Conan Doyle writes about a gas attack in 1915.

Source A

> Poison gas was a dreadful weapon which most cruelly affected the victim. The Germans won ground using the methods of the mass murderer. Their great army became in a single day an object of tremendous horror and great contempt.

2. Discuss the attitude of the author of **Source A** towards the use of poison gas.   **4**

In **Source B** a British soldier writes about the aftermath of a gas attack.

Source B

> We have heaps of gassed soldiers. The poor things are burnt all over with great blisters and blind eyes all glued together. They speak in a merest whisper saying their throats are closing and they will choke.

3. How fully do **Sources A** and **B** describe the use of gas in the First World War?

   You must use **your own knowledge** and give reasons for your answer. 5

[END OF CONTEXT IIB]

Marks

UNIT II—INTERNATIONAL COOPERATION AND CONFLICT

CONTEXT C: 1930s–1960s

SECTION A: KNOWLEDGE AND UNDERSTANDING

During the 1930s there was a growing danger of a new world war.

(Note: for this answer you should write a short essay of several paragraphs.)

1. How important as a cause of the Second World War was

EITHER

(a) German rearmament in the 1930s?   **8**

OR

(b) Hitler's actions against Czechoslovakia, 1938–1939?   **8**

SECTION B: ENQUIRY SKILLS

The following sources reflect different attitudes to the Cuban missile crisis of 1962.

Study the sources carefully and answer the questions which follow.
You should use your own knowledge where appropriate.

Source A is part of a broadcast by US President J. F. Kennedy on 22 October, 1962.

Source A

These new Soviet missile sites on Cuba include medium-range ballistic missiles which are capable of striking Washington DC or any other city in the south eastern part of the United States. Other sites not yet finished are designed for intermediate-range ballistic missiles capable of striking most of the major cities in the Western Hemisphere.

2. How fully does **Source A** explain the US view of the Cuban missile crisis?

   You must use **your own knowledge** and give reasons for your answer.   **5**

Marks

Source B is part of a message from the Russian leader, N. Khrushchev, to President Kennedy on 27 October, 1962.

Source B

> You want to make your country safe. This is understandable, but Cuba too wants the same thing. All countries want to make themselves safe. But how are we, the Soviet Union, to assess your actions when you have surrounded the Soviet Union with military bases. This is no secret. Your rockets are situated in Turkey. You are worried about Cuba because it is only 90 miles from America. But Turkey is right next to us.

3.   Discuss the attitude of the author of **Source B** towards America.   **4**

[END OF CONTEXT IIC]

Marks

UNIT III—PEOPLE AND POWER

| CONTEXT A: USA 1850–1880 |

SECTION A: KNOWLEDGE AND UNDERSTANDING

| Americans believed it was their "Manifest Destiny" to fill the continent with white settlers. |

1. Describe some of the problems faced by the native Americans ("Indians") as a result of white westward expansion.   **4**

| Life for everyone in the Reconstruction South was difficult. |

2. Explain why there was widespread discontent in the South after the Civil War.   **4**

SECTION B: ENQUIRY SKILLS

The following sources relate to the election of Lincoln and the new Republican government.

**Study the sources carefully and answer the questions which follow.
You should use your own knowledge where appropriate.**

Source A is a poster published by the Republican party in 1860.

Source A

THE UNION

IT MUST AND SHALL BE PRESERVED

Rally round the flag, boys
Rally once again!!!

FOR PRESIDENT OF THE UNITED STATES

ABRAHAM LINCOLN

who says:

"My main object is to save the Union and not either to save
or destroy slavery. What I do about slavery and the colored
race I do because I believe it helps to save the Union."

Marks

3.   How useful is **Source A** as evidence of Lincoln's policies if elected as President?   **4**

Source B is taken from South Carolina's "Declaration of Secession" published in December, 1860.

Source B

> A line has been drawn across the Union. All the states North of that line have been united in the election of a President who is against slavery. The Republican Party will become the government and the South shall be excluded. A war will be waged against slavery until slavery shall cease throughout the United States. With Lincoln as President, the equal rights of the states will be lost. The slaveholding states will no longer have the power of self government. The American Government will have become their enemy.

4.   Discuss the views expressed in **Source B** about the effects of Lincoln's election.   **4**

5.   To what extent does **Source B** disagree with **Source A** about Lincoln's policies?   **4**

[END OF CONTEXT IIIA]

Marks

UNIT III—PEOPLE AND POWER

CONTEXT B: INDIA 1917–1947

SECTION A: KNOWLEDGE AND UNDERSTANDING

> Gandhi said, "It is the old method of divide and rule. We divide and you rule."

1. Describe some of the divisions amongst Indian people living under British rule.   **4**

> In August 1942, Congress declared a "Quit India" campaign.

2. Explain why the Congress Party gained support from the Indian population.   **4**

SECTION B: ENQUIRY SKILLS

The following sources give evidence about Gandhi's opposition to British rule.

**Study the sources carefully and answer the questions which follow.
You should use your own knowledge where appropriate.**

Source A is a British cartoon which appeared on the day that Gandhi's Salt March began in March, 1930.

Source A

A FRANKENSTEIN OF THE EAST

GANDHI: "Remember—no violence; just disobedience"
INDIAN GENIE: "And what if I disobey you?"

Marks

3. How useful is **Source A** as evidence of British attitudes towards Gandhi's non-violent tactics?   **4**

Source B is a letter from Gandhi to the British Viceroy in March, 1930.

Source B

> While I think British rule of India is a curse, I do not intend harm to a single British person. Nothing but organised non-violence can check the organised violence of the British government. This non-violence will be expressed through civil disobedience. My ambition is to convert the British people and make them see the wrong they have done to India. Civil disobedience will be peaceful and with it we will combat evils such as the salt tax. This letter is not intended as a threat, but I feel it is my duty as a civil resister to send it to you.

4. Compare the views about civil disobedience in **Sources A** and **B**.   **4**

5. Discuss Gandhi's attitude towards British rule in India as shown in **Source B**.   **4**

[END OF CONTEXT IIIB]

Mark:

UNIT III—PEOPLE AND POWER

CONTEXT C: RUSSIA 1914–1941

SECTION A: KNOWLEDGE AND UNDERSTANDING

> Although the peasants had been freed from serfdom, things had not improved for most of them.

1. Describe some of the hardships faced by Russian peasants before 1917.   **4**

> Within six months Lenin was urging that the time was right for the Bolsheviks to seize power.

2. Explain why, by October 1917, Lenin thought the time was right for the Bolsheviks to seize power.   **4**

SECTION B: ENQUIRY SKILLS

The following sources relate to collectivisation in Russia between 1927 and 1934.

Study the sources carefully and answer the questions which follow.
You should use your own knowledge where appropriate.

Source A is from Stalin's speech to the Party Congress in 1927.

Source A

> The way to improve agriculture is to turn the small and scattered peasant farms into large united farms based on the common cultivation of the land. The way ahead is to unite the small peasant farms gradually but surely, not by pressure but by example and persuasion, into large farms based on common, cooperative collective cultivation of the land. There is no other way to improve.

3. Discuss Stalin's attitude towards agricultural change in Russia.   **4**

Marks

Source B is a Soviet government photograph from the 1930s showing a Communist Party worker talking to peasants about collectivisation.

Source B

4. How useful is **Source B** as evidence of how collectivisation was achieved in Russia?   **4**

Source C is from "Dreams, Plans and Nightmares" by Tony Howarth.

Source C

> Some peasants in the villages, especially the poorer ones, were in favour of collectivisation. So were the local rural soviets; and 25 000 trusted party men from the cities were sent to encourage collectivisation. They also threatened and bullied and where peasants resisted, the security police turned up with armed men and machine guns.

5. To what extent do **Sources B** and **C** agree about the methods used to bring about collectivisation?   **4**

[END OF CONTEXT IIIC]

Marks

UNIT III—PEOPLE AND POWER

CONTEXT D: GERMANY 1918–1939

SECTION A: KNOWLEDGE AND UNDERSTANDING

> When the news of the Treaty reached the German people the reaction was one of predictable anger.

1. Describe some of the reasons for German anger over the Treaty of Versailles.   **4**

> Historians still debate why so many people supported the Nazi state.

2. Explain why many Germans supported the Nazis between 1933 and 1939.   **4**

SECTION B: ENQUIRY SKILLS

The following sources give evidence about the treatment of the Jews in Germany.

**Study the sources carefully and answer the questions which follow.
You should use your own knowledge where appropriate.**

Source A shows Jewish children being made a fool of at school in 1935. The wording on the blackboard says "The Jews are our greatest enemy. Beware of the Jews."

Source A

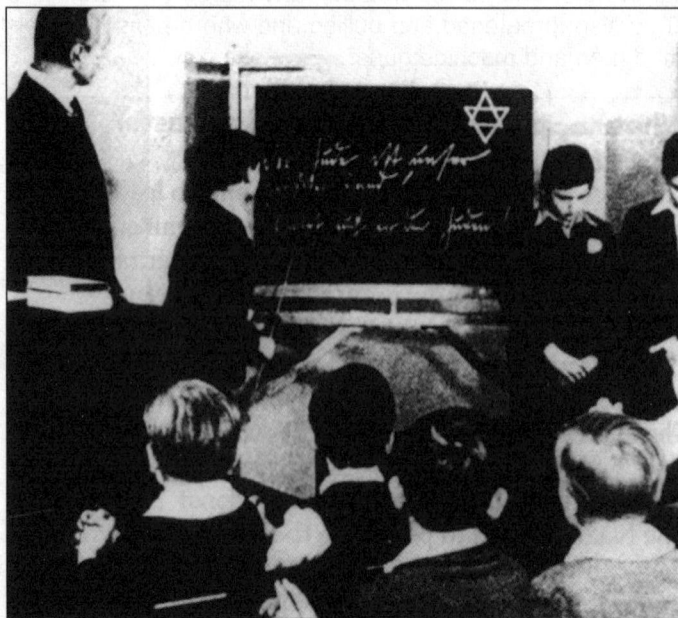

3. How useful is **Source A** as evidence of the treatment of Jewish children in Nazi Germany?   **4**

Marks

Source B is an extract from the memoirs of a Jewish woman, Alice Solomon. It describes the treatment of a Jewish child at school in 1935.

Source B

> One day she came home humiliated. "It was not so nice today", she said. What had happened? The teacher had placed the Aryan children to one side of the classroom, and the non-Aryans to the other. Then the teacher told the Aryans to study the appearance of the others and to point out the marks of their Jewish race. They stood separated as if by a gulf. Children who had played together as friends the day before were now enemies.

4. To what extent do **Sources A** and **B** agree about the treatment of Jewish children at school in Nazi Germany?   **4**

In **Source C** a Jew from Munich describes the treatment he received on Crystal Night in November 1938.

Source C

> The mood among the Christian population in Munich is wholly opposed to the action against the Jewish population. I personally encountered much sympathy and compassion from all sides. Aryan people from the area offered to shelter my family for the night. Despite the harsh ban on sales to Jews, grocers asked Jews whether they needed anything. Bakers delivered bread to Jewish families, ignoring the ban.

5. Discuss the attitudes of the people in Munich towards the Jews, as shown in **Source C**.   **4**

[END OF CONTEXT IIID]

[END OF QUESTION PAPER]

[BLANK PAGE]

[BLANK PAGE]

[BLANK PAGE]

[BLANK PAGE]

[BLANK PAGE]

Pocket answer section for SQA History Standard Grade General Level 2000 and 2001

© Copyright 2001 Scottish Qualifications Authority, All Rights Reserved
Published by Leckie & Leckie Ltd, 8 Whitehill Terrace, St Andrews, Scotland, KY16 8RN
tel: 01334 475656, fax: 01334 477392, hq@leckieandleckie.co.uk, www.leckieandleckie.co.uk

INTRODUCTION

Knowledge and Understanding

Answers are given as bullet points. Candidates must always respond in full sentences, addressing the correct process and actually responding to the item: either describing, explaining or assessing importance (preferably with reference to other important factors).

In the 8 mark, extended writing exercise the candidate should structure the response appropriately with an introduction, six points of relevant, supporting evidence and a conclusion which clearly addresses the specific requirements of the item.

Enquiry Skills

Evaluation of evidence: normally, only 1 mark will be allocated <u>for each type</u> of evaluation offered: contemporaneity; authorship; content; purpose etc.

Comparing Sources: 1 mark is allocated for a simple comparison; 2 marks for a developed comparison. Examples of both types are given.

Assessing attitude: 1 mark is allocated for each assessment or explanation.

Putting a source in context: full marks can only be awarded if recall is used.

Selecting evidence to address an issue: this is the only area where a candidate can supply bullet points or list evidence.

Providing a conclusion: full marks cannot be awarded unless the candidate uses presented evidence + recall + balance in their response.

History General Level— 2000

Unit I—Context A: 1750s–1850s

Section A

1. The candidate describes who could vote in 1792 using presented evidence such as:

    - men (males only) or no women
    - landowners or wealthy estate owners
    - a very small number of men (those with the correct property qualification)
    - fictitious voters who had been given the (dubious) right to vote

    and from **recalled evidence** such as:

    IN SCOTLAND

    - town councillors: a few, wealthy **men**
    - parchment barons with a wadsett (developed point)
    - Scottish property qualification = £200 Scots
    - over 21 years old

    IN ENGLAND

    - wealthy male landowners with property qualification of 40/- freehold
    - variety of borough voter: Scot and lot; potwalloper; nomination; pocket

2. The candidate explains why Scotland's population shifted with reference to such evidence as:

    from the source

    - Scotland moving from rural to industrial society
    - rural society was affected by evictions
    - Highland Clearances caused Highlanders to move
    - growing centres of industry attracted people to work
    - growing towns attracted people to live

    and from recalled evidence such as:

    - new farming techniques abolished run rig and fewer farmers needed
    - sheep farming drove out Highlanders

History General Level—2000

- Industrial Revolution brought factories and jobs to towns
- Rural Society affected by shortages

Section B

3. The candidate evaluates Source C using evidence such as:
   - contemporaneity:
     primary source from period of change in rural housing
   - authorship:
     a 19th century traveller with first hand knowledge
   - purpose:
     a tour manual highlighting living conditions
   - bias/accuracy:
     traveller might not see all types of housing
   - limitation:
     limited to Lowland description only; Cobbett might have been entertained in wealthy homes;
   - content:
     useful information on one type of Lowland housing

4. The candidate identifies evidence of agreement in Source C such as:
   - house has changed from old type
   - houses no longer simple with dirt-floor
   - house now large and solid—not a "hut"
   - houses built of stone and slate
   - houses have other amenities: barns; out buildings (for animals)
   - houses now have chimneys (fire-places)

   The candidate identifies evidence of disagreement in Source D such as:
   - house still made of turf and peat
   - houses still had inside dung heap
   - animals still lived inside a house
   - house full of smoke from open fire
   - house still had earthen floor
   - cooking still done on open fire

5. The candidate offers a conclusion to the issue using evidence such as:

   presented evidence
   - Lowland housing was better in 1850 than 1750
   - old types of housing had largely been replaced
   - rich farmers lived in some style
   - some Highland housing still primitive

   and from recalled evidence such as:

   early housing conditions:
   - but and ben; inseat and spence
   - primitive materials
   - box beds
   - low doors and small, unglazed windows
   - improved drainage; improved ventilation
   - new villages built by improvers

   later housing conditions improved:
   - fine homes of landed gentry
   - bedrooms; kitchens; cooking ranges
   - change varied across class and across Scotland;
   - toilets still not common in 1850

Unit I—Context B: 1830s–1930s

Section A

1. The candidate gives an account of the methods used by the militant Suffragettes using **presented evidence** such as:
   - interrupting meetings of Prime Minister Asquith
   - smashing windows
   - setting fire to letter boxes

   and **recalled evidence** such as:
   - slashing paintings in art galleries
   - cutting telephone wires
   - burning/bombing buildings
   - chaining themselves to railings
   - violent methods/vandalism
   - hunger striking/refusing to eat

History General Level— 2000

2. The candidate explains the reasons for migration to towns and cities using **presented evidence** such as:
   - farmers driven out by agricultural improvement
   - small farms disappeared
   - farmers were evicted
   - to become mechanics

   and **recalled evidence** such as:
   - machines replaced men in the countryside
   - effects of Highland Clearances
   - pull effects of cities: attractions of town life
   - employment available in towns
   - housing available in towns
   - moving to be near relations

Section B

3. The candidate evaluates Source C using evidence such as:
   - contemporaneity:
     primary source from 1918–from a period of changes in rural housing
   - content:
     details of rural housing problems
   - authorship:
     Royal Commission report—an official record/document or eyewitness evidence
   - accuracy:
     official report based on eyewitness evidence
   - purpose:
     description of rural housing to reveal conditions

4. The candidate identifies evidence from Source C to show that 19th Century rural housing had not improved such as:
   - unsatisfactory sites
   - badly constructed cottages
   - damp farm dwellings
   - insufficient water supplies
   - bad drainage
   - inadequate refuse removal
   - unfit habitation in Highlands and Islands
   - lack of decent sanitary conditions

   The candidate identifies evidence from Source D to show that rural housing had improved using evidence such as:
   - built of stone or brick
   - slate roofs
   - stone or wooden floors
   - proper fireplace
   - proper water supply

5. The candidate offers a conclusion to the issue using evidence such as:

   from **presented evidence**
   - low walls and doors
   - earth floors
   - damp
   - small windows (lack of ventilation/light)

   BUT
   - stone/brick building
   - slate roofs
   - stone/wooden floors
   - running water
   - fireplaces

   and from **recalled evidence**
   - improvement in other areas
   - better facilities
   - better sanitation

   BUT
   - housing for unmarried men still poor (bothies)
   - unmarried women lived in attics above farm house
   - many farmers did not improve cottages
   - houses still lacked basic amenities: toilets, sewerage
   - many moved to towns rather than suffer rural conditions
   - rural Highland housing remained largely primitive
   - lack of power (electricity)

History General Level— 2000

Unit I—Context C: 1880s–Present Day

Section A

1. The candidate gives an account of the methods used by the militant suffragettes using **presented evidence** such as:

   - interrupting meetings of Prime Minister Asquith
   - smashing windows
   - setting fire to letter boxes

   and **recalled evidence** such as:

   - slashing paintings in art galleries
   - cutting telephone wires
   - burning/bombing buildings
   - chaining themselves to railings
   - violent methods/vandalism
   - hunger striking

2. The candidate explains the reasons why the population in Scottish towns increased using **presented evidence** such as:

   - people moved from the countryside
   - immigrants (people from overseas)
   - people looking for work

   and **recalled evidence** such as:

   - people left Highlands and the Borders area to move to towns
   - better education led to move to towns for good jobs
   - to find a "better" life
   - to seek employment in booming industry such as shipbuilding/ mining/factories
   - any acceptable reasons for population increase eg diet, hygiene

Section B

3. The candidate evaluates Source C using evidence such as:

   - contemporaneity:

     from the 1940s
     from a period of changing housing

   - authorship:

     first hand knowledge of council housing estates

   - content:

     detail on council housing estates

   - purpose:

     to describe council housing

   - accuracy:

     only mentions Wishaw

   - bias:

     as a local council report may be one-sided/written in a positive light

4. The candidate identifies evidence in Source C of good living conditions in a council housing estate such as:

   - all houses have gardens
   - good accommodation (kitchen, bathroom, living room)
   - spacious (2 or 3 bedrooms) housing has good/separate facilities eg bathroom/kitchen
   - better than old slum housing
   - good amenities; parks; play areas

   The candidate identifies evidence in Source D that council housing did not provide good living conditions such as:

   - built as cheaply as possible
   - built on poor land
   - built in large estates
   - crammed together
   - lacked shops and facilities nearby
   - housed problem families
   - built near gas works/railway lines

5. The candidate offers a conclusion to the issue using evidence such as:

   from **presented evidence**:

   - council houses offered good accommodation
   - separate kitchen and living room
   - better facilities

   BUT

   - estates were built on poor land
   - suffered from lack of close facilities
   - had problem families "dumped" there

History General Level—2000

and from **recalled evidence** such as:

- council houses had gas/ electricity
- had hot/cold running water
- more space than "single ends"
- built on open ground out of town centre
- tended to be of same design
- could lack sense of community
- could have high rents

Unit II—Context B: 1890s–1920s

Section A

1. The candidate explains the consequences of the alliance system using **presented evidence** such as:

   - Europe divided into two armed camps
   - great power blocs developed
   - Germany, Austria Hungary and Italy formed the Triple Alliance
   - Triple Alliance dominated Central Europe
   - France and Russia were scared of the Triple Alliance

   and **recalled evidence** such as:

   - France and Russia concluded an alliance
   - Britain made Entente Cordiale with France
   - Britain concluded a Triple Entente
   - War came closer as a result of tensions caused by alliances
   - in 1914 the alliances pulled its members into war
   - encouraged countries to build up armaments
   - brought GB out of isolation
   - Germany felt encircled

2. The candidate assesses the importance of the role of women during World War One using **presented evidence** such as:

   - they were needed
   - took over from men
   - entered previously male-only jobs

- released men for war work
- kept important services going
- worked in vital areas: railways, factories, police
- worked on the farms/in the Land Army

and **recalled evidence** such as:

- other types of work done by women to release men for the front
- munition work to produce shells
- working as VADs or nurses to treat war wounded
- entering the services
- impressed men and showed what women could do
- raised women's self esteem
- helped to gain the vote for women in 1918
- made vital contribution to the war effort
- encouraged men to go to war

Section B

3. The candidate identifies the viewpoint of the authors of the Covenant using **evidence** such as:

   - League was to settle disputes
   - League was to keep peace/ prevent war
   - League was to reduce armaments
   - consider any member going to war on another as an enemy of the whole League
   - cut off trade with any member breaking the Covenant

4. The candidate compares Sources C and D using **evidence** such as:

   Both Sources agree that the League was to prevent war/keep the peace:

   - Source C: League is to prevent war
   - Source D: a peace keeping body

   Both Sources agree the League is to settle disputes:

   - Source C: aim is to settle disputes
   - Source D: in favour of peace and prevent war

History General Level— 2000

Both Sources agree members had to follow the rules of the Covenant:

- Source C: rules are laid out to be obeyed
- Source D: no-one must break the rules of the Covenant

Both Sources agree that members who break the rules should be punished:

- Source C: punishments laid out for breach of Covenant
- Source D: take action against a member who breaks the rules

Both Sources agree that members had to act together:

- Source C: rules for all to follow
- Source D: all members required to act together

Sources agree that armaments were not to be completely abolished:

- Source C: national armaments reduced
- Source D: members still kept armaments

Sources disagree about success of the League:

- Source C: aims are to keep peace
- Source D: it was a failure as peace keeping body
- Source C: members must act together
- Source D: members rarely acted together

Unit II—Context C: 1930s–1960s

Section A

1. The candidate explains the reasons for German rearmament using **presented evidence** such as:
   - Germany had been made to disarm (against her will)
   - Germany needed to be strong for defence
   - to build up weapons
   - job opportunities would result

and **recalled evidence** such as:

- unfairness of German disarmament at Versailles
- no one else had disarmed
- restoration of German pride
- increase military aggression
- Germany felt threatened (encircled)

2. The candidate explains the importance of rationing using **presented evidence** such as:
   - prevents food being wasted
   - avoids putting sailors at risk
   - increases war effort
   - releases ships for other imports
   - ensures equal and fair shares for all

and **recalled evidence** such as:

- release fuel for warships
- need to conserve food due to imports falling
- prevention of uncertainty/ hoarding
- avoidance of queues
- control of food prices
- ships free to carry armaments and essential war supplies

Section B

3. The candidate evaluates the opinion expressed in the source using **evidence** such as:
   - Critical of UN (of its effectiveness)
   - UN not an independent body
   - UN not a united organisation
   - UN not a good peacekeeping body
   - UN only furthers American interests
   - unhappiness at Russian role

4. The candidate evaluates degree of agreement between Sources C and D with reference to **evidence** such as:

Both Sources agree Russia and USA were members of the UN:

- Source C: Russian/American membership
- Source D: rivalry of Soviet Union and United States

Both Sources agree that UN was set up as a peace-keeping body:

- Source C: UN is (meant to be) peace-keeping body

History General Level—2000

– Source D: asks how effective it was as a peace-keeping body

Both Sources agree that Russians and Americans were rivals:

– Source C: Russian speaker calls it an "organisation for Americans"
– Source D: rivalry of Soviet Union and United States

Only Source C accuses Americans of aggression

Only Source D mentions using the veto/blocking decisions

Unit III—Context A: USA 1850–1880

Section A

1. The candidate describes how the Southern States seceded with reference to **presented evidence** such as:
   – South Carolina first to break away
   – South Carolina decided it did not want to be part of the Union and declared independence
   – Other states followed suit
   – Meeting held to declare independence and set up a new nation

   and from **recall** such as:
   – Cotton states which followed were: Mississippi; Alabama; Georgia; Florida; Louisiana; Texas
   – Eight delegates met at Montgomery Alabama to declare independence
   – a provisional (later permanent) constitution adopted
   – Jefferson Davis elected President of the new Confederacy
   – Alexander Stephens elected Vice President

2. The candidate explains why Lincoln wanted to avoid a Civil War using evidence such as:

   from **presented evidence**:
   – War would destroy the existing government

   – War is a "momentous issue": a terrible thing
   – he had made an oath to protect the existing government (Union)
   – North and South are not enemies but friends

   and from **recalled evidence** such as:
   – War would lead to the break up of the United States
   – War would lead to friction between North and South and divide the nation
   – There is no real squabble: slavery would not be interfered with where it existed
   – Differences could be settled peacefully
   – War would lead to strife and bloodshed and deaths
   – Lincoln's oath was as President of the **United** States

Section B

3. The candidate evaluates Source C in terms of such features as:
   – authorship:
     a 19th century American author
   – contemporaneity:
     drawn in the 1870s
   – purpose:
     to give an impression of an "Indian" night attack
   – content:
     shows "Indians" creeping up at night on a wagon train drawn into a circle
   – accuracy:
     typical White person's view: "Indians" attacking at night; "Indians" acting sneakily; white settlers have expected attack and drawn up wagons into a circle
   – bias/limitation:
     An artist's impression—might be exaggerated

History General Level— 2000

4. The candidate compares Sources C and D using evidence such as:

    Both Sources agree that "Indians" engage in warlike pursuits:

    –   Source C shows "Indians" attacking with weapons
    –   Source D calls them "warlike"

    Sources disagree about methods of fighting:

    –   Source C shows them hiding in the grass/at night
    –   Source D says they attack openly

    Sources disagree about nature of the "Indian":

    –   Source C shows them sneaking up in a night attack/attacking a wagon train
    –   Source D says they are kind, honest and reliable

    Only Source D says "Indians" are religious

    Only Source D gives reasons for an attack: to prevent hunting grounds

5. The candidate assesses to what extent Source E describes American attitudes to "Indians" using **presented evidence** such as:

    –   White settlers regarded the land as theirs
    –   "Indians" had no real right to the land
    –   "Indians" were on a par with the wild dogs
    –   "Indians" were just a part of the landscape
    –   "Indians" were an obstacle to be overcome
    –   overcoming all obstacles such as the "Indians" was part of American (Manifest) Destiny

    and **from recalled evidence** such as:

    –   "Indians" do not use land properly
    –   "Indians" are lazy
    –   "Indians" do not deserve the land
    –   "Indians" are savages

Unit III—Context B: India 1917–1947

Section A

1. The candidate describes the way the Untouchables were treated using **presented evidence** such as:

    –   regarded as outside the caste system
    –   only allowed to do unpleasant jobs
    –   not allowed to drink from the same well as others
    –   had to live in slums

    and from **recalled evidence** such as:

    –   bear the mark of their caste
    –   forced to live apart from others
    –   not allowed into same temples
    –   no inter-marriage allowed

2. The candidate gives an explanation of Gandhi's opposition to British rule using **presented evidence** such as:

    –   made slaves of the Indians
    –   destroyed Indian way of life
    –   only interested in what is good for British trade

    and from **recalled evidence** such as:

    –   made millions of Indians poor
    –   ran the country for benefit of Britain
    –   Britain set up a large civil service and army
    –   Britain imposed "unfair" taxes—eg on Salt
    –   Britain unwilling to give Indians a greater say in running of India
    –   British treated Indians as inferior

Section B

3. The candidate evaluates the usefulness of the source using evidence such as:

    –   contemporaneity:

        primary source from inter-war period

    –   authorship:

        British newspaper advert

History General Level— 2000

- content:

  useful detail on India's economic value

- limitation:

  only deals with trade and employment (economic importance)

- purpose:

  purpose is to promote British-Indian trade

- accuracy:

  possible bias as an advert

4. The candidate evaluates the completeness of the evidence in the source about why Britain wanted to retain control of India using **presented evidence** such as:

   - India was the largest importer of British goods
   - huge Indian orders provided employment in Britain
   - India provided Britain with range of foodstuffs
   - India provided Britain with harbours for shipping

   and/or from **recall** such as:

   - strategic/military importance
   - the "jewel" in Britain's empire
   - British business interests in India
   - serious violence feared if British left

5. The candidate compares the Sources using **evidence** such as:

   Both Sources are concerned with British interests in India:

   - Source C deals with British interests
   - Source D stresses British interests

   Both Sources stress economic value of India:

   - Source C stresses financial value
   - Source D talks of India as "valuable"

Both Sources stress the importance of trade with India:

- Source C shows the importance of trade
- Source D talks of "building trade"

Both Sources stress importance of shipping trade:

- Source C stress importance of shipping trade
- Source D talks of "shipping interests"

Only Source C deals with actual trading commodities

Only Source C talks about employment offered through Indian trade

Unit III—Context C: Russia 1914–1941

Section A

1. The candidate explains reasons for discontent with the Provisional government using **presented evidence** such as:

   - Russian army suffering defeats
   - German army better equipped
   - Food prices rising
   - Kerensky offering no immediate solutions
   - Lenin's policies appeal more

   and from **recalled evidence** such as:

   - continuation of the war
   - Russians were war weary
   - Lenin offered an end to the war and better solutions
   - Bolshevik propaganda was stirring up discontent
   - Land reform delayed

2. The candidate explains the reasons for the Bolshevik victory using **presented evidence** such as:

   - Reds controlled heartland
   - Reds controlled communications
   - many ordinary Russians supported them
   - Whites not united

History General Level— 2000

and **recalled evidence** such as:

- Bolsheviks controlled vital areas: Moscow; Petrograd
- White armies were widely dispersed
- Nature of White divisions
- White army angered many through atrocities
- Trotsky's leadership
- Reds' political ideals

Section B

3. The candidate evaluates Source C using **evidence** such as:
   - contemporaneity:
     primary source produced at the time of the purges
   - content:
     clearly blames Stalin for the deaths
   - accuracy:
     shows the scale of the killing
   - purpose:
     designed as anti-Stalin propaganda
   - bias:
     drawn by anti-Communist—likely bias
   - limitation:
     author is an exile—not living in Russia

4. The candidate evaluates the degree of agreement between Sources C and D using **evidence** such as:

   Both Sources agree that killing was a method used by Stalin:
   - Source C shows pile of skulls
   - Source D talks of corpses

   Both Sources agree that there were many deaths:
   - Source C shows a huge pyramid of skulls
   - Source D talks of many corpses and the frequency of deaths

Both Sources agree that there was an indifference towards deaths/ victims:
- Source C shows a proud Stalin "gloating" over the skulls
- Source D says that the dead were left to freeze/mixed with cement

Both Sources agree that Stalin was implicated:
- Source C shows Stalin
- Source D talks of Stalin's camps

Only Source C shows result of the purges.

Only Source D talks about people being worked to death.

5. The candidate evaluates the completeness of the source explaining Stalin's reasons for the purges using **presented evidence** such as:
   - getting rid of those who spoke their mind
   - eliminating opposition to Stalin
   - eliminating "wrong" classes
   - eliminate potential rivals for leadership

   and **recalled evidence** such as:
   - Stalin wishing no challenge to his authority
   - Stalin wanting sole and personal credit for industrial success
   - consolidate his own position
   - Stalin's personality (paranoia)
   - fear of foreign attack/counter revolution
   - Kirov murder and aftermath

Unit III—Context D: Germany 1918–1939

Section A

1. The candidate gives an account of the Spartacist uprising using **presented evidence** such as:
   - Spartacists wanted a Communist Germany (like Russia's)
   - took place in Berlin
   - Ebert (Government) used force to crush the rising
   - hundreds slaughtered
   - leaders killed

History General Level—2000

and **recalled evidence** such as:

- leaders were (Karl) Liebknecht and (Rosa) Luxemburg
- took place in January 1919
- Spartacists seized public buildings
- called for a general strike
- barricaded streets
- Ebert was the Chancellor (PM)
- role of Noske (Defence Minister)
- government used the Freikorps

2. The candidate explains Hitler's success in winning power using **presented evidence** such as:

- Depression created the right conditions
- Hitler's emotional appeal to people's fears and hates
- Hitler's use of propaganda to win mass support
- Hitler's use of brutality and control (violence and intimidation)

and **recalled evidence** such as:

- Hitler's attacks on Versailles appealed to many
- Hitler's attack on Weimar/democracy appealed to many
- Hitler's attacks on Communism appealed to many
- detail of economic hardship and its effects
- detail on methods of propaganda
- Hitler's powers of oratory
- Hitler made promises

Section B

3. The candidate evaluates the source using **evidence** such as:

- contemporaneity:

  source based on statistics from the time being studied (1930s)
- content:

  gives evidence about concentration camp prisoners and deaths as methods of dealing with opposition

- authorship:

  from Nazi sources so some reliability—statistical presentation
- accuracy:

  possibility of bias—either exaggeration or "playing down" true figures
- purpose:

  evidence of Nazi repression
- completeness/limitation:

  consistent with other evidence of Nazi methods

  more information required for accuracy

4. The candidate evaluates the degree of agreement between Sources C and D using **evidence** such as:

Both Sources agree that concentration camps were used for prisoners of the Nazis:

- Source C shows table of prisoners in Nazi concentration camps
- Source D says "we were prisoners of the Nazis"

Both Sources agree that the number of prisoners increased between 1933 and 1939:

- Source C shows numbers going up between those dates
- Source D talks of numbers increasing from 1933 (to 1939)

Both Sources agree that many thousands were imprisoned by 1939:

- Source C shows 130,000 imprisoned in 1939
- Source D talks of "many thousands"

Only Source C gives death figures

Only Source D gives reasons for being sent to a camp

Source C gives more accurate figures

5. The candidate evaluates the fullness of the explanation of opposition to the Nazi government using **presented evidence** such as:

- opposition in the church was ineffective and powerless

History General Level—2000

- opposition in the Civil Service was unable to do anything
- Nazis were too powerful and had a stranglehold
- opposition groups lacked power and energy

and **recalled evidence** such as:

- problems experienced by Churchmen such as Neimoller, Bonhoeffer and Galen
- problems experienced by Socialist and Communist opposition
- groups like the Edelweiss pirates not organised effectively
- difficulties of opposition in the face of Nazi violence: SS, Gestapo, camps etc
- difficulties such as Nazi support and use of spies
- army oath to Hitler made opposition from the military difficult
- Nazis controlled propaganda
- Nazis censored the media

History General Level—2001

Unit I—Context A: 1750s–1850s

Section A

1. The candidate explains the effects of better farming technology using evidence such as:
   - new technology replaced wind power
   - Meikle's threshing machine replaced the unpredictable use of the wind
   - Small's plough cut the soil easily
   - Small's machine had a metal cutting blade
   - Small's plough could be pulled by just 2 horses

and from recall such as:

- old hand-labour, winnowing techniques
- old threshing methods using the flail
- Meikle's machine used mechanical flails
- new technology saved time
- new technology saved human effort
- old ploughs: wooden, clumsy, pulled by team of oxen
- seed drills replacing broadcast sowing
- scythe replacing sickle
- reaping machines slowly replacing scythe
- farmers could choose when to perform farming tasks

2. The candidate assesses the importance of good water supplies using evidence such as:
   - pumps were much used (by many people)
   - water was often polluted
   - cholera was caused by polluted water
   - 50,000 died of cholera in 1848

and **recalled evidence** such as:

- bad water spread disease/killed people
- existing water supply was insufficient
- bad sanitation affected water supplies
- infected sewage found its way into the water supply
- overcrowding and poor living conditions also spread disease
- houses had no running water
- lack of medical knowledge meant disease from bad water was usually fatal

Section B

3. The candidate evaluates Source C using **evidence** such as:
   - authorship:

     eyewitness account of changes in food supply

History General Level—2001

- contemporaneity:

  primary source from someone living in the early 19th Century

- content:

  useful content on changes in food supply and infant mortality

- purpose:

  designed to inform as a memory of life at a time of change

- accuracy:

  written as an autobiography, looking back, so could be affected by memory

- limitation:

  only one man's account of one area **or** only one cause of population growth

4. The candidate selects evidence for the issue from Source C, such as:

    - food supplies in the 1760s were poor
    - little meat and few vegetables in 1760s
    - people ate very little before improvements in food took place by 1814
    - people ate better by 1814
    - more babies were born healthy in 1814
    - fewer babies died in 1814

    The candidate selects evidence to show other factors from Source D, such as:

    - demand for labour (more children are needed)
    - rise in the birth rate
    - earlier marriages and thus more children
    - better wages meant people could afford children
    - advances in hygiene
    - advances in medical care

5. The candidate agrees or disagrees that the population of Scotland rose between 1760 and 1820 as a result of improvements in food supply using the evidence presented above and from relevant, recalled evidence such as:

    For the issue:

    - fall in the death rate
    - results of new farming
    - nutrition from potatoes, vegetables
    - exponential increase—population explosion

    for other factors:

    - increase in desire for children (better conditions; country at peace)
    - control of disease (smallpox)
    - disappearance of disease (plague; malaria)
    - better child care
    - better hospital facilities
    - control of drinking
    - lack of contraception

Unit I—Context B: 1830s–1930s

Section A

1. The candidate explains the ways in which rail travel improved between 1850 and 1930 using **presented evidence** such as:

    - average speeds increased (to 60 mph)
    - London to Aberdeen took only 8·5 hours (62 mph)
    - locomotives improved
    - railway competition encouraged improvements
    - heating introduced into carriages

    and **recalled evidence** such as:

    - earlier speeds were slower
    - earlier conditions were primitive
    - lavatories introduced into some trains
    - sleeping cars introduced
    - restaurant cars introduced
    - improvements made to carriage design
    - lighting introduced into carriages
    - better track and signalling

History General Level— 2001

- Tay Bridge and Forth Bridge reduced travelling time North
- locomotive technology improved

2. The candidate assesses the importance of the lack of clean water using **presented evidence** such as:
   - people unable to wash without clean water
   - typhus results from dirty conditions/lice
   - typhus killed many people
   - cholera and typhoid fever caused by contaminated water
   - over 100,000 people killed by cholera
   - polluted food also killed

   and **recalled evidence** such as:
   - houses did not have running water
   - water often had to be bought
   - open sewers polluted water supply
   - lack of sewers and drains
   - further connection between cholera and polluted water
   - early Public Health Acts ineffective
   - other possible causes of disease/ ill health

Section B

3. The candidate evaluates Source C using **evidence** such as:
   - authorship:
     Scottish eyewitness account
   - contemporaneity:
     primary source from period of population growth in 19th Century
   - content:
     useful information on diet and population
   - purpose:
     A Reminiscence: to inform others
   - accuracy:
     memoir of of one individual who experienced the events
     a memory of events: possible flaw

- limitation:
  just one area of Scotland covered/one person's opinion

4. The candidate identifies evidence for the issue from Source C, such as:
   - eating habits have changed
   - diet improved: more meat, vegetables
   - more food available: more baker's shops
   - people are healthier
   - people are living longer
   - families are larger

   The candidate identifies other factors from Source D, such as:
   - declining death rate
   - drop in infant mortality
   - mothers healthier
   - general improvement in standard of health
   - babies healthier
   - more babies surviving

5. The candidate suggests a conclusion using the evidence presented above and from relevant, recalled evidence such as:

   For the issue:
   - better farming methods
   - developments in railways for transporting food
   - greater choice of food

   } Resulting in healthier population, people living longer, larger families

   for other factors:
   - better medicine: vaccination
   - better child care
   - disappearance of some diseases
   - better living conditions: sewerage; water supply
   - Public Health Acts
   - better hygiene: cotton clothes; soap

History General Level— 2001

Unit I—Context C: 1880s–Present Day

Section A

1. The candidate explains how motor transport has affected lives in the countryside using **presented evidence** such as:

   - rural folk/people from the countryside can visit towns
   - children can go to school by bus
   - Doctors can visit countryside (to treat people)
   - roads have been built in the countryside
   - beauty spots have been damaged
   - motor accidents
   - problem with safety on the roads
   - cars make people lazy

   and **recalled evidence** such as:

   - fresh food can be delivered
   - people can commute
   - farmers can take produce to market
   - pollution problems
   - traffic jams

2. The candidate assesses the importance of clean water using **presented evidence** such as:

   - would help to stop disease spreading
   - water has to be clean and free from disease
   - sewage must not contaminate water
   - sewerage also important
   - by 1900 most towns had a clean supply

   and **recalled evidence** such as:

   - cholera and typhoid further reduced
   - other factors are important: housing; medical care; hygiene.

Section B

3. The candidate evaluates Source C using **evidence** such as:

   - authorship:

     well informed reporter

   - contemporaneity:

     primary source from 1960—during period of population rise in question

   - purpose:

     designed to inform—to record facts

   - content:

     links diet to population growth

   - accuracy:

     unlikely to be biased—a statistical account: accurate figures

   - limitation:

     figures for Aberdeenshire towns only; only 1 factor mentioned.

4. The candidate selects evidence for the issue from Source C, such as:

   - town dwellers better fed
   - more money was spent on food
   - more fruit in the diet
   - school meals
   - free milk
   - uncontaminated milk available

   The candidate selects other evidence from Source D, such as:

   - babies live beyond 1 year (infant mortality dropped)
   - TB reduced
   - antibiotics available
   - fewer mothers died at childbirth
   - women went on to have families

5. The candidate suggests a conclusion supported by presented evidence such as that presented above and from relevant, recalled evidence such as:

   - food transport
   - farming improvements
   - other health factors: eg inoculation
   - better hospital treatment
   - National Health improvements
   - movement into towns
   - immigration
   - improved hygiene: use of soap, disinfectant

History General Level— 2001

Unit II—Context B: 1890s–1920s

Section A

1. The candidate describes fighting in the First World War using **presented evidence** such as:
    - use of trenches
    - shrapnel shells
    - use of troops going into a frontal attack
    - heavy casualties resulted

    and from **recalled evidence** such as:
    - artillery barrage
    - troops going "over the top"
    - details of trench warfare
    - machine guns
    - other weapons: eg rifles, grenades
    - assault on enemy positions
    - new technology: gas, tanks
    - ineffectiveness of frontal attacks
    - use of barbed wire

2. The candidate assesses the importance of Clemenceau's views on how Germany should be treated, using **presented evidence** such as:
    - his anti German attitude was important
    - he decided that Germany should be told what to do
    - he wanted to treat Germany firmly
    - he wanted to make sure France would not be invaded again

    and from **recalled evidence** such as:
    - he was one of the Big Four who negotiated the treatment of Germany
    - Germany was severely treated
    - Germany was dictated to (by the Diktat)
    - examples of severe treatment of Germany
    - examples of attempts to keep Germany weak
    - contribution of other important representatives at Versailles

    - Wilson's more idealistic approach overshadowed by Clemenceau's views

Section B

3. The candidate determines the attitudes the poster (Source C) is encouraging with reference to **presented evidence** such as:
    - Britain is the cause of continued fighting
    - Britain is causing suffering
    - Britain is stopping them living their lives in peace
    - Britain is their deadly enemy
    - Together, Germans can still win the war/beat Britain

4. The candidate assesses the completeness of Source D with reference to **presented evidence** such as:
    - a lot of turnips eaten
    - luxury goods disappeared
    - rich could still afford luxuries
    - necessities rationed/soap rationed

    and from **recalled evidence** such as:
    - effects of the blockade
    - further effects of rationing
    - food riots
    - use of ersatz food
    - horrors of air-raids
    - loss of relatives
    - problems caused by inflation
    - effects of (Spanish) influenza

Unit II—Context C: 1930s–1960s

Section A

1. The candidate assesses the importance of Churchill's leadership using **presented evidence** such as:
    - he was in charge of defence
    - he inspected fortifications
    - he started the Home Guard
    - he gave lots of orders

    and **recalled evidence** such as:
    - his speeches boosted morale
    - he negotiated US aid (lend-lease)

History General Level— 2001

- the coalition government united the country
- and other possible factors, eg:
- RAF defeated Luftwaffe in Battle of Britain
- air-raid precautions and evacuations helped protect civilians

2. The candidate describes the effects of the atomic bomb using **presented evidence** such as:

- light burned eyes
- people incinerated
- 70,000 killed

and **recalled evidence** such as:

- many survivors burned
- blast destroyed most of city
- thousands died from radiation sickness
- contributed to surrender of Japan
- started nuclear age/arms race

Section B

3. The candidate evaluates the attitude of Germans as shown in Source C using such evidence as:

- thought the situation was dreadful
- alarmed at no public services working (gas, electricity, water)
- panic amidst the chaos
- only thought was to escape
- thought the situation was frightening/terrifying

4. The candidate evaluates the completeness of the source with reference to **presented evidence** such as:

- some did feel the war was ending
- some felt that Hitler would lose
- some felt that Nazism should be abandoned
- some felt Nazis were criminals
- some felt Nazis should be opposed/resisted

and from **recalled evidence** such as:

- typical of some feeling in 1943
- some earlier attitudes were optimistic
- typical of those who resisted the Nazis: religious groups; youth groups; July Bomb plotters
- air raids did affect morale
- many Germans still continued to support the war effort
- most Germans did not support resistance
- many were frightened to oppose the Nazis
- Nazi regime made opposition difficult

Unit III—Context A: USA 1850–1880

Section A

1. The candidate describes the attitude of native Americans (Indians) to the land using **presented evidence** such as:

- land is very valuable
- land cannot be destroyed (is there for ever)
- land gives life (in the same way as the sun and water)
- land cannot be sold

and from **recalled evidence** such as:

- given by the Great White Spirit
- everyone should only take what they need from the land
- everyone should live in harmony with the land
- land should not be exploited
- land belongs to no one
- land was held in trust

2. The candidate explains why slavery was a cause of the Civil War using **presented evidence** such as:

- southern, slave owning states fighting for right to manage own affairs
- northern states were opposed to slavery
- southern states wanted to opt out of the Union
- northern states determined to preserve the Union

History General Level— 2001

and from **recalled evidence** such as:

- north was generally abolitionist
- horrors of slave life
- economic differences between industrial North and plantation South
- fears about destruction of Southern way of life
- fanatical leaders unwilling to compromise

Section B

3. The candidate evaluates Source C using evidence such as:

   - authorship:

     newspaper cartoon: sympathetic to Blacks/against White terrorism

   - contemporaneity:

     primary source from 1873—at time of Reconstruction/White terrorism

   - content:

     shows Blacks are being oppressed/methods of white terrorists

   - accuracy:

     northern newspaper: hostile to KKK and White terrorists

   - purpose:

     to criticise treatment of Blacks in the Reconstruction south

   - reliability:

     content matches other evidence: KKK carrying weapons, lynchings . . .

4. The candidate assesses the completeness of Source C using **presented evidence** such as:

   - show typical costume of the KKK: white hoods etc
   - shows KKK smiling: happy in his work?
   - shows KKK heavily armed

- shows KKK dealing in death (hand on skull)
- shows KKK in league with other white supremacists (White League)
- shows KKK suppressing the Blacks

and from **recalled evidence** such as:

- KKK usually shown as grim terrorists
- does not show other KKK symbols: fiery cross
- does not show clandestine/secret nature of the organisation
- KKK usually operated at night
- no evidence of hierarchy/rank/ senior members
- no evidence of social background of KKK

5. The candidate assesses agreement between the Sources with reference to features such as:

   Both sources agree that KKK used terror against Blacks:

   - Source D says "set up to terrorise Black people"
   - Source C shows Blacks cowering beneath armed KKK figure

   Both sources agree that arson was used against Black people:

   - Source D says KKK "did not hesitate at arson"
   - Source C shows burning building

   Both sources agree that schools for Black people were attacked:

   - Source D says "favourite target was burning local school"
   - Source C shows school house in flames (and a discarded school book)

   Both sources say hanging was used against the Blacks:

   - Source D says "Many Blacks were hanged"
   - Source C shows a hanging body

   Both sources agree about how KKK dressed:

   - Source D says "ghostly white clothes"
   - Source C shows figure in white, hooded sheet

History General Level— 2001

Both sources agree about the secrecy of the KKK:

- Source D says "secret society"
- Source C shows hooded (clandestine) figure

Only Source D says KKK frightened Blacks by carrying a burning cross

Only Source D says torture was used

Only Source C says Blacks were being treated worse than when they were slaves

Unit III—Context B: India 1917–1947

Section A

1. The candidate explains why British control of India was of benefit, using **presented evidence** such as:

   - an important part of the British Empire
   - supplied many Indian goods which were exported to Britain
   - enabled many British goods to be sent to India
   - Britain's largest single market
   - British cotton and/or heavy engineering products were sent to India

   and **recalled evidence** such as:

   - examples of Indian goods sent to Britain (cotton, rice, jute, tea, wheat)
   - provided employment
   - provided jobs in the Raj
   - non-economic reasons: racial superiority/imperialism "civilising mission"

2. The candidate describes the events at Amritsar using **presented evidence** such as:

   - took place in the Jallianwalla Bagh
   - 10,000 demonstrators met British troops
   - a massacre happened

   and **recalled evidence** such as:

   - British troops commanded by General Dyer
   - Dyer acting on orders of British Governor
   - British army opened fire without warning
   - Indian crowd was unarmed
   - crowd was protesting for home rule
   - incident took place in the knowledge of previous violence (4 Europeans killed)
   - many Indians were unaware of extended laws/martial law
   - result was 379 Indians killed; 1208 wounded

Section B

3. The candidate evaluates Source C using evidence such as:

   - authorship:

     an actual Muslim League poster

   - contemporaneity:

     published in 1946: the year of Direct Action Day

   - content:

     shows areas claimed by the Muslim League

   - purpose:

     reveals feelings and intentions of Muslim League (emotive language)

   - limitation:

     map does not show that some of claimed areas were mixed Hindu/Muslim (eg Punjab, Bengal)

   - accuracy:

     shows attitude of most Muslims

4. The candidate assesses the completeness of Source C with reference to such **presented evidence** as:

   - reveals attitudes of Muslims
   - shows Muslims wanted partition
   - shows Muslims were prepared to fight and die for Partition
   - shows the areas Muslims wanted to break away

History General Level— 2001

and from **recalled evidence** such as:

- does not reveal Hindu attitudes
- does not reveal complications caused by divisions in caste, wealth, religion, language
- does not reveal attitude of British in India
- does not reveal attitude of Sikhs
- does not show problems over alignment of proposed borders
- does not reveal attitude of people in the Punjab or Bengal

5. The candidate compares agreement/disagreement between the sources with reference to features such as:

   The sources agree that Muslims were encouraged to fight for Pakistan:

   - Source C: "We shall fight for Pakistan"
   - Source D: "Leaders encouraged Muslims to fight"

   The sources agree (to some extent) about deaths:

   - Source C: "We shall die; take it or perish"
   - Source D mentions 5000 deaths in Calcutta

   - only Source D describes Muslim attacks on Hindus
   - only Source D describes Muslims looting Indian shops
   - only Source D mentions it provoked Hindu retaliation

Unit III—Context C: Russia 1914–1941

Section A

1. The candidate explains why the Tsar had so much power using **presented evidence** such as:

   - he was chief of the armed forces
   - he was head of the Orthodox Church

   - he was believed to be chosen by God

   and **recalled evidence** such as:

   - he was an autocrat—could rule as he wished
   - he had no parliament to control his power
   - he used the Okhrana, secret police, which crushed opposition
   - censorship of newspapers and books
   - used army/Cossacks to crush unrest
   - exiled opponents to Siberia
   - most Russians belonged to Orthodox Church (and accepted Tsar's powerful position)

2. The candidate describes the way civilians suffered during the Civil War using **presented evidence** such as:

   - thousands of workers shot
   - peasants flogged
   - widespread looting

   and **recalled evidence** such as:

   - women publicly flogged
   - peasants crops burned
   - widespread famine
   - food rationing introduced in towns
   - many villages and homes destroyed
   - many forced to go and fight

Section B

3. The candidate evaluates the source using evidence such as:

   - authorship:

     from official government figures/a graph easy to "read"

   - contemporaneity:

     figures from within the period of NEP

   - content:

     shows that production did increase 1922–25

   - accuracy:

     possible government propaganda

   - purpose:

     figures aimed to show that NEP was working

History General Level— 2001

- limitation:

  only shows some areas of productivity

4. The candidate assesses the completeness of the evidence in Source C using **presented evidence** such as:
   - iron production increased
   - grain production increased
   - cattle increased in number
   - NEP partly successful
   - more cattle in 1925 than pre-war
   - iron production did not increase to pre-war figure
   - grain production did not increase to pre-war figure

   and from **recalled evidence** such as:
   - land under cultivation increased
   - Kulaks did particularly well
   - starvation became less of a problem
   - foreign specialists recruited
   - other industrial production did not increase to pre-war figures
   - Russia did not fully catch up with the West
   - concentration on heavy industry (but it did not recover)
   - NEP men encouraged private trade
   - light industry improved due to increased consumer demand

5. The candidate compares the effects of the NEP as shown in Sources C and D using evidence such as:

   Sources agree that animal production increased after 1922:
   - Source C shows an increase from 45 m to 62 m
   - Source D says more animals appeared

   Sources agree that industrial output increased after 1922:
   - Source C shows iron production increasing
   - Source D says industrial production began to climb

   Sources agree that food production improved:
   - Source C shows increase in grain/cattle
   - Source D says that starvation was less of a problem

   Sources disagree that grain production increased to pre World War One levels:
   - Source C show that by 1925 grain had not reached level of 1913
   - Source D says that grain production was back to 1913 level

   Only Source D mentions enthusiasm of the peasants/workers

Unit III—Context D: Germany 1918–1939

Section A

1. The candidate describes the aftermath of the Munich Putsch using **presented evidence** such as:
   - Hitler accused of high treason
   - Hitler put on trial
   - Hitler's trial lasted 24 days
   - Hitler made front page news
   - Hitler's words were read by millions

   and **recalled evidence** such as:
   - Hitler was arrested
   - Hitler sentenced to five years
   - Hitler imprisoned in Landsberg Castle
   - Hitler spent 9 months in prison
   - Hitler wrote Mein Kampf while in prison
   - Hitler decided to use more political methods

2. The candidate explains why the Weimar Republic was unpopular in 1932 using **presented evidence** such as:
   - could not solve unemployment
   - new elections did not help/ democracy was weak
   - blamed for Versailles
   - criticised by Hitler

   and **recalled evidence** such as:
   - many blamed Weimar for defeat in World War One

History General Level— 2001

- many blamed Weimar for accepting reparations
- many blamed Weimar for inflation
- many people preferred Nazi policies

Section B

3. The candidate assesses the usefulness of Source C in terms of evidence such as:

    - authorship:

      produced by Nazis

    - contemporaneity:

      primary source produced during the Nazi era

    - content:

      useful detail relating to the activities of Hitler Youth members

    - purpose:

      to persuade young people to join the movement

    - accuracy:

      Nazi propaganda—everyone enjoying themselves

    - consistency/limitation:

      backed up/contradicted by other evidence: eg compulsion to join

4. The candidate compares agreement in the sources using evidence such as:

    Both sources agree that there was a range/variety of activities:

    - Source C shows a lot of activities
    - Source D says "range of activities"

    Both sources agree that members wore (were pleased to wear) uniforms:

    - Source C shows children (proudly?) in uniform
    - Source D says "some enjoyed the uniforms"

    Both sources agree that marching and discipline took place:

    - Source C shows a group marching in order

    - Source D says "children enjoyed marching and discipline"

    Both sources agree that Hitler Youth went camping:

    - Source C shows tents/campers
    - Source D says "outdoor events such as camping"

    Both sources agree about appeal of musical events/parades:

    - Source C shows drums/ marching
    - Source D says "music was . . . part of parades"

5. The candidate assesses the completeness of Source D using **presented evidence** such as:

    - Hitler Youth offered outdoor activities
    - Hitler Youth activities were exciting
    - Nazi youth movements involved attractive pursuits
    - Hitler Youth members wore uniforms
    - some enjoyed drill and some marching/military activities
    - some enjoyed (military) music

    and from **recalled evidence** such as:

    - Hitler Pimpfen attracted young members
    - League of German Maidens attracted girls
    - girls trained to be good Aryan mothers
    - Nazi Education/teachers
    - Nazi propaganda
    - brainwashing into Nazi ideology

Pocket answer section for SQA History Standard Grade Credit Levels 2000 and 2001

Published by Leckie & Leckie Ltd, 8 Whitehill Terrace, St Andrews, Scotland, KY16 8RN
tel: 01334 475656, fax: 01334 477392, hq@leckieandleckie.co.uk, www.leckieandleckie.co.uk

INTRODUCTION

Knowledge and Understanding

Answers are given as bullet points. Candidates must always respond in full sentences, addressing the correct process and actually responding to the item: either describing, explaining or assessing importance (preferably with reference to other important factors).

In the 8 mark, extended writing exercise the candidate should structure the response appropriately with an introduction, six points of relevant, supporting evidence and a conclusion which clearly addresses the specific requirements of the item.

Enquiry Skills

Evaluation of evidence: normally, only 1 mark will be allocated <u>for each type</u> of evaluation offered: contemporaneity; authorship; content; purpose etc.

Comparing Sources: 1 mark is allocated for a simple comparison; 2 marks for a developed comparison. Examples of both types are given.

Assessing attitude: 1 mark is allocated for each assessment or explanation.

Putting a source in context: full marks can only be awarded if recall is used.

Selecting evidence to address an issue: this is the only area where a candidate can supply bullet points or list evidence.

Providing a conclusion: full marks cannot be awarded unless the candidate uses presented evidence + recall + balance in their response.

History—Credit Level 2000

Unit 1—Context A: 1750s–1850s

Section A

1. The candidate assesses to what extent medical knowledge contributed to population increase with reference to factors such as:

    – better medicine stopped people from dying
    – better medicine allowed babies to live
    – better medicine allowed women to have more babies
    – better hospitals kept more people alive
    – medical training and enlightened doctors kept people alive
    – inoculation helped control disease

    and with possible reference to other factors such as:

    – better farming and increased food supply
    – introduction of new foodstuffs
    – improved transport and markets
    – better child care
    – earlier marriages
    – larger families
    – some diseases died out naturally
    – improved lifestyles caused larger families
    – some immigration from Ireland
    – new diseases (cholera, typhus) still baffled medical science

History—Credit Level 2000

2. The candidate describes the changes brought about by the coming of textile factories such as:

    -   old domestic system of craft work and small scale employment declined
    -   factory employees worked for a (small) wage
    -   factories meant established, long hours
    -   factories were full of machinery
    -   factories were noisy and full of health hazards
    -   factories mass produced material
    -   used a lot of child labour

Section B

3. The candidate evaluates Sources A and B using evidence such as:

    Source A:

    -   contemporaneity:

        primary from the time of farming change in the late 18th/early19th century

    -   authorship:

        Scottish, eyewitness account of farming changes

    -   content:

        detail of agriculture change written to record the remarkable changes which have occurred in an "interesting time"

        accuracy:

        only one man's memories; in one area Scotland only

    Source B:

    -   contemporaneity:

        secondary, from reputable historians who have studied the evidence/benefit of hindsight

    -   accuracy:

        information backs up that in A; tenants and lairds both improved;

    -   content:

        new ploughs introduced; tenant farmers improved farms

4. The candidate identifies evidence in the sources to support the view that technological changes during the period 1750-1850 improved the lives of Scottish farmers, such as:

    From Source A:

    -   old farming methods were inefficient
    -   new, improved ploughs were introduced to treat the land
    -   new drainage methods recovered farm land
    -   more money was made from farming
    -   some tenants got long leases
    -   some tenant farmers were able to buy land
    -   farmers could now experiment

    From Source B:

    -   new techniques were labour saving
    -   Chain plough replaced Old Scot's Plough and was lighter to operate
    -   scythes and reaping machines made harvesting easier than sickles
    -   better farming/more produce fed a growing nation

    From Source C:

    -   improved farming methods

    The candidate identifies contradictory evidence such as:

    From Source A:

    -   only some farmers got rich or got long leases (not all succeeded)
    -   some farmers could not afford to change

    From Source B:

    -   change was slow to come

    From Source C:

    -   some small farmers were evicted
    -   some decent, hard working cottagers had to leave the land
    -   some evicted workers had to seek jobs in factories

History—Credit Level 2000

5. The candidate offers a balanced conclusion to the issue of how far technological changes benefited Scottish farmers using evidence such as:

From presented evidence

- labour saving techniques
- new implements
- better yields
- surplus and profit produced
- scientific, business farming
- not everyone benefited
- some small farmers were evicted

and from recall

- failure of run rig farming
- enclosure movement
- other examples of technology eg sowing machines; threshing machines
- examples of improved standard of living
- not all farmers could afford new technology
- long leases gave farmers incentives

Unit I—Context B: 1830s–1930s

Section A

1. The candidate assesses the importance of the rising birth rate as a factor contributing to population growth using evidence such as:
   - early marriages due to changes in employment market
   - family size increasing due to prosperity/security
   - lack of contraception
   - falling death rate
   - better food supplies
   - improved public health
   - better medical knowledge
   - better housing standards
   - immigration from Ireland

2. The candidate describes changes in working conditions for farmers using evidence such as:
   - insecure working conditions
   - low wages throughout the period
   - migrant labour
   - periods of boom and bust
   - some migration to towns
   - better scythes
   - mechanisation used for harvesting/threshing/use of steam power
   - tractors/technology/oil/petrol replacing horses

3. The candidate evaluates Sources A and B using evidence such as:

Source A

contemporaneity:

primary source from 1840s during early railway changes

authorship:

specialist railway magazine—well informed

content:

details of effects of railways

bias/exaggeration:

possible as a pro-railway source

purpose:

to praise railways

Source B

contemporaneity:

primary source: a memoir looking back to early railways

authorship:

an eyewitness directly involved

content:

useful evidence of opposition to railways

accuracy:

one person's experience; memory may be hazy

History—Credit Level 2000

4. The candidate identifies evidence in the sources to support the view that the railways were universally welcomed such as:

Source A

- country will be opened up
- cheap travel
- fast travel
- agriculture will benefit from transportation
- land values will increase
- business commuting will be eased

Source C

- cheap travel for workers
- people could live further from work—in the countryside/ suburbs
- industry could relocate to its advantage
- holiday resorts were opened up
- industrial products could be carried cheaply

The candidate identifies evidence in the sources to suggest that railways were *not* universally welcomed using evidence such as:

Source B

- some people frightened of train travel
- dangers apparent to some
- health would be injured
- cows would refuse to be milked (scared by noise)
- horse trade would be ruined

Source C

- canal trade adversely affected
- coaching trade adversely affected
- countryside became built up

5. The candidate offers a balanced conclusion on the issue using relevant evidence such as:

From the Sources:

- fast, cheap transport
- increase in land values
- transport of fresh produce/ agricultural goods
- transport of industrial goods
- suburban living possible
- cheap, available transport for all
- holiday resorts
- some fear of railways: for people and animals
- quality of life changed (towns grew, pattern of living changed)
- coaching died out
- canal system declined

and from recall such as:

- transport of fresh fish from the coast
- industrial transport advantages
- creation of jobs
- leisure travel
- newspaper deliveries
- penny post
- trade affected
- air pollution
- environmental damage
- destruction of countryside

Unit I—Context C: 1880s–Present Day

Section A

1. The candidate gives an account of the ways the employment of women changed after 1918 using recalled knowledge such as:

- war had opened up more opportunities
- women used experience of work gained during World War One
- it was more acceptable for women to work
- more women entered the professions
- birth control allowed women to plan families and follow a career
- new inventions/technology opened up opportunities in the workplace
- better pay
- sex discrimination acts
- women lost jobs when soldiers returned

History—Credit Level 2000

2. The candidate makes a judgement on the importance of medical care causing population rise using evidence such as:
   - school medical inspection spotted problems early
   - new medicines (eg penicillin) kept people alive
   - vaccinations against killer diseases
   - X-rays spotted disease early
   - National Insurance provided workers with medical care
   - maternity clinics were set up
   - NHS provided better health care
   - better qualified nurses and doctors

Section B

3. The candidate evaluates Sources A and B using evidence such as:

   Source A:
   - contemporaneity:
     primary source written during the 1970s when impact of motor transport was growing
   - authorship:
     the viewpoint of someone in a remote location
   - bias:
     one sided source mentioning bad effects only
   - content:
     details of damage done by cars to people's lives
   - accuracy:
     only one person's opinion

   Source B:
   - authorship:
     value as a secondary source from knowledgeable historian with benefit of hindsight
   - bias:
     one sided account on benefits of motorised transport

   - content:
     gives relevant details on the impact of motor transport

4. The candidate identifies evidence which supports the issue such as:

   Source B:
   - freedom to go where people want
   - goods can be delivered door to door
   - deliveries can be made at any time
   - reduced costs of transportation

   Source C:
   - transporting goods much easier
   - standard of living improved

   The candidate identifies evidence which contradicts the issue such as:

   Source A:
   - makes people lazy
   - reduces standard of living (expense of motoring)
   - leads to closure of local shops
   - public transport reduced so non car-owners suffer

   Source C:
   - serious road traffic problems
   - pollution of the atmosphere

5. The candidate offers a balanced conclusion on the impact of motor transport using such evidence as:

   from presented evidence
   - easier/cheaper to transport goods
   - contribution to better standard of living
   - life difficult without a car
   - congestion on roads
   - expense of motoring
   - pollution

History—Credit Level 2000

and from recall

- demand for cars created important industrial opportunities
- remote communities benefited from road network
- employment opportunities provided (eg garages)
- tourism boosted
- increase in road traffic accidents
- other forms of transport declined
- led to greater social divide: wealthy moved into suburbs
- services like superstores built on the edge of towns: not available to all
- town centres declined

Unit II—Context B: 1890s-1920s

Section A

1. The candidate gives an explanation of the importance of the assassinations in causing the war using evidence such as:
    - assasinations in Bosnia blamed on Serbian Group
    - Austria-H used assassinations as an excuse to hand ultimatum to Serbia
    - Serbia refused to agree to all points
    - Austria-H declares war on Serbia wanting to destroy it as nationalistic base
    - Russia mobilises in support as Big Slav Brother
    - background to Russian–Austro Hungarian rivalry in Balkans
    - alliance system comes into play
    - Germany as part of Triple Alliance declares war on Russia
    - Franco-Russian Alliance involves France
    - Germany declares war on France
    - part played by the Arms/Naval race

2. The candidate explains the reservations which the major powers had about the Treaty of Versailles using evidence such as:
    - France thought it was too lenient: wanted Germany dismembered/to lose more territory
    - USA was concerned it was too harsh and would lead to bitterness and revenge
    - Britain was divided in opinion although many wanted punishment of Germany
    - Italy was disappointed at its gains
    - Germany thought it was too harsh
    - Germany said it was a diktat
    - Germany was alarmed at prospect of reparations
    - German hated War Guilt clause

Section B

3. The candidate evaluates the usefulness of the source using evidence such as:
    - authorship:
      photograph usually accurate record of an event
    - contemporaneity:
      primary source during World War One
    - purpose:
      shows conditions on the Western Front
    - content:
      detailed evidence: mud, shell-holes, treeless, shattered landscape; soldiers working
    - accuracy:
      only one section of the Western Front photograph shows aftermath of battle, not actual fighting

History—Credit Level 2000

4. The candidate compares the sources using presented evidence such as:

- Sources agree that Western Front was "a sea of mud"
  Source A shows lots of water and mud;
  Source B says "vast stretch of mud"
- Sources agree that water-filled shell-holes were common
  Sources A shows holes of water;
  Source B says "water-filled shell-holes".
- Sources agree about shattered, treeless landscape
  Source A shows featureless terrain;
  Source B says "not a tree, not a blade of grass, vast stretch"
- Sources agree about men labouring on
  Source A shows men labouring with duck boards;
  Source B says "men trudging on"
- Only Source B refers to effect on morale
- Only Source A shows results of a battle (casualty on a stretcher)

5. The candidate evaluates the attitude of the soldier using evidence such as:

- says mud and rain were dreadful
- registers detachment at being wounded
- happy that he has escaped death
- relief at being "out of it"
- realises that the battle has failed
- considers his involvement as pointless
- very quickly forgets failure

Unit II—Context C: 1930s-1960s

Section A

1. The candidate assesses the importance of the attack on Poland using evidence such as:

- Britain and France had made a commitment to Poland
- Chamberlain realised that appeasement had failed
- British public opinion had had enough of Hitler
- it became clear Hitler wanted to dominate Europe
- clear Hitler would use force.
- Britain and France honoured their agreement by declaring war on 3/9/39
- earlier Czech crisis showed Hitler could not be trusted

2. The candidate explains the causes of the Berlin crisis using evidence such as:

- Berlin divided after World War Two
- background to friction over zones of influence/Berlin corridor
- despite Russian objections Western powers introduced new currency into West Berlin
- Stalin suspected Western powers wanted to create separate West German State
- Russian retaliation—cutting off rail and road links in Berlin Blockade
- Western Powers began airlift
- Western Powers warned against interference with supply planes
- incidents regarding air-supply planes
- Russians called off blockade: 12th May 1949

History—Credit Level 2000

Section B

3. The candidate evaluates the source using evidence such as:

    - contemporaneity:
      primary source from wartime
    - authorship:
      British source from wartime newspaper
    - content:
      implies British bombing is in retaliation for German bombing
    - purpose:
      implies Allied bombing is successful
    - accuracy: only one city being shown (Berlin?); does depict effects of an air attack
    - purpose: propaganda to raise British morale
    - bias/exaggeration is evident in the **cartoon**

4. The candidate compares the sources using evidence such as:

    Both sources agree that Germany was bombed:

    - Source A shows Germany under attack
    - Source B talks about the bombing of Berlin/Germany

    Both Sources agree there was great destruction in places like Berlin:

    - Source A shows huge explosion and cowering leaders
    - Source B says: damage was severe

    Both Sources agree that Britain bombed in retaliation:

    - Source A is captioned "A Taste of their Own Medicine"
    - Source B says: British were getting their own back on the enemy

    Sources are different in their depiction of the scale of the bombing

    - Source A shows only one city
    - Source B mentions Berlin and Hamburg

    Sources disagree about the effect of bombing on German morale

    - Source A implies that morale/confidence is low
    - Source B says: morale did not break

    Sources disagree about the effect of the bombing:

    - Source A implies that British bombing was a great success (bringing German leaders to their knees)
    - Source B says that bombing campaign did not have a very successful effect.

5. The candidate evaluates the attitudes shown in the Source using **evidence** such as:

    - fear at the air raid siren
    - panic in the mad dash for shelter
    - forgetfulness in the panic and mad dash
    - anxiety over the possibility of gas attacks and bombing
    - hatred of the Germans
    - apparent calm (feigned indifference)
    - need to protect children
    - worry at possibility of being bombed
    - uncertainty of not knowing what was to happen

Unit III—Context A: USA 1850–1880

Section A

1. The candidate describes the problems and difficulties in the Reconstruction South with reference to such evidence as:

History—Credit Level 2000

(a) **For "Whites"**

- severe food shortage and deprivation
- feelings of humiliation and defeat
- coming to terms with freed slaves
- racial tensions existed
- some whites against black schools
- some slave owners generous to ex slaves
- some bitter at free slaves taking their jobs
- old master class and attitudes remained
- bitterness at Black Codes
- some whites joined Ku Klux Klan
- hatred of military government
- hatred of carpetbaggers
- discontent at Freedmen's Bureau

(b) **For "Freed Slaves"**

- slaves now free under 14th amendment but still difficulties
- 15th amendment (right to vote) largely ignored
- poor application of Black Codes (Black marriages allowed (not with whites), Blacks could sue in courts, Blacks could own property).
- few amenities/schools for freed slaves
- Freedmen's Bureau
- black slaves now legally free but often treated the same
- racial tension and codes not applied
- some whites attacked   blacks and regarded them still as inferior
- some ex slaves still working on plantations in poor conditions
- some ex slaves wanted away from plantations

- many blacks drifting or begging
- starvation a real problem
- some blacks attacked by Ku Klux Klan
- freed slaves were often unemployed

Section B

2. The candidate assesses the completeness of Source A using **presented evidence** such as:

- slavery was the cause of the Civil War
- many Northerners wanted slavery abolished
- abolition of slavery was good and was patriotic
- President Lincoln was in favour of the control of slavery
- Southerners felt threatened by such attitudes
- opposition in the South to Lincoln's election as President

and **recalled evidence** such as:

- other slavery related issues: Kansas-Nebraska Act; Missouri Compromise, John Brown's Raid
- tariff disputes
- North-South divide in industrial and social areas

3. The candidate compares the Sources using evidence such as:

Sources agree that slavery was a cause of the Civil War

- Source A: slavery is the cause of the unhappy affair
- Source B: among the causes of war was . . . restrictions against slave trade/President . . . against slavery

Sources agree that many (Northerners/Republicans) wanted control of slavery

- Source A: large majority in the North want slavery wiped out
- Source B: Republican-appointed officials would enforce restrictions against slave trade/spread abolition propaganda/contain slavery

History—Credit Level 2000

Sources agree that many thought the abolition of slavery was a good thing:

- Source A: good people want slavery wiped out
- Source B: slavery is a moral evil

Sources agree that Lincoln was against slavery:

- Source A: Our new President will fulfil aim (of wiping out slavery)
- Source B: President dedicated to notion that slavery was evil

Sources agree that anti-slavery activity would result from Lincoln's election:

- Source A: President will wipe out slavery
- President and his officials will spread abolition propaganda/ restrict slavery

Sources disagree about Lincoln's attitude to slavery:

- Source A says Lincoln will abolish it
- Source B: Lincoln will contain it

Sources disagree about slavery's role as a cause of the war

- Source A says it is *the* sole cause
- Source B says it is amongst the causes

Unit III–Context B: India 1917—1947

Section A

1. (a) The candidate gives a full account of life in India under the British Raj for the British using such evidence as:

   - many enjoyed a pleasant, pampered existence
   - many had Indian servants
   - exercised authority over the "inferior" Indians
   - British customs were transported to India (cricket, polo)

   - many adopted home life as if back in Britain
   - exercised power: eg ran the Indian Civil Service
   - ran the Indian army
   - civil servants signed on for 30 years service
   - developed business interests
   - operated the railways
   - struggled to cope with difficult climate

   (b) The candidate gives a full account of life in India under the British Raj for the Indian population using evidence such as:

   - British rule established order
   - communications improved, travelling easier (railways)
   - irrigation canals helped in fight against famine
   - employment provided (Army, Civil Service)
   - disease brought under control
   - people began to feel Indian—not members of a particular caste or sect
   - Indians felt they were heavily taxed
   - villagers complained at imports of Lancashire textiles
   - felt British did not understand their ways/culture
   - Indians blamed British for their poverty
   - annoyed at being discriminated against
   - annoyed at having to wear British cloth
   - political opponents of British imprisoned

2. The candidate sets the source in context using **presented evidence** such as:

   - Muslim propaganda
   - urges Muslims to join in Direct Action Day
   - urges Muslims to fight for their freedom

History—Credit Level 2000

and from **recalled evidence** such as

- set in the context of Labour government favouring independence for India
- Muslims demanding freedom (a separate state)
- British attempts at a compromise failed
- suggestion to create a federal India with Muslim devolved control; rejected
- Viceroy has asked Nehru (leader of the largest party) to form a government
- Muslims showing opposition to new government

3. The candidate compares Sources A and B using evidence such as:

- both sources want freedom for their people
  Source A = "dedicate lives to the cause of freedom",
  Source B = "India free of foreign domination"
- both sources claim peace is best
  Source A = "they offered peace";
  Source B = "dreamed of an India at peace"
- Source A is now recommending Military Action / "Might" = violence
- Source B remains committed to peace
- Source A only mentions Muslims/wanted a separate Muslim state
- Source B wants a united India

Unit III—Context C: Russia 1914–1941

1. (a) The candidate gives a full account of War Communism and its effects using evidence such as:
   - War communism policies: grain requisition
   - armed food detachments were sent into the countryside to seize food
   - hoarders were shot by the Cheka
   - widespread famine killed millions
   - workers were sent to any part of the country
   - peasants opposed the government and refused to surrender food
   - Russian economy brought to brink of disaster
   - Russian industry declined
   - thousands left the cities
   - after Kronstadt—war communism dropped

   (b) The candidate gives a full account of the New Economic Policy and its effects using evidence such as:
   - NEP introduced after Kronstadt suppressed
   - aim to encourage peasants to grow more food
   - surplus grain would be sold to Nepmen
   - taxation in kind
   - richer peasants (Kulaks) permitted to hire labourers
   - state control remained in large industries: railway, coal, steel
   - private enterprise was allowed in small businesses
   - foreign investment encouraged
   - NEP was a success; more food produced
   - NEP was an industrial success: production up
   - many communists were opposed to NEP

2. The candidate evaluates the completeness of Source A using **presented evidence** such as:

   - view of one Russian general serving at the front in 1917
   - accurate assessment of the condition of the army: no hope of victory
   - overthrow of the government would be welcome

History—Credit Level 2000

and **recalled evidence** such as:

- Russian army defeats
- millions of conscripts were unhappy
- shortages of weapons
- shortages of food and equipment
- detail of imminence of revolution: unhappiness in Russia and at the front
- poor treatment of wounded
- increasing number of desertions
- Tsar (as C-i-C) blamed for defeats
- Bolshevik propaganda

3. The candidate compares the Sources using evidence such as:

- both agree that conditions were difficult:
  Source A talks about disastrous conditions;
  Source B mentions difficulties
- both agree that the soldiers blamed the government:
  Source A: no victory until the government is changed;
  Source B: the men are criticising the government
- Source A goes further than Source B in dealing with army spirit (morale)
- Source A goes further (is more critical) than Source B and says that Revolution is imminent/would be welcomed
- Source B mentions additional factors contributing to discontent: eg Rasputin
- only Source B deals with the fact that soldiers are informed and actively seeking information

Unit III—Context D: Germany 1918–1939

1. (a) The candidate gives a full account of Nazi policy towards the Jews using evidence such as:

- anti-Jewish propaganda
- dismissal of Jewish officials from government posts
- difficulties for Jewish professionals
- boycotting of Jewish shops
- attacks on Jewish properties
- Nuremberg Laws
- removal of human and civil rights
- concentration camps
- Kristallnacht
- way open for Holocaust

(b) The candidate gives a full account of Nazi policy towards young people using evidence such as:

- education controlled
- subjects "Nazified"
- separate sex roles emphasised
- education as indoctrination
- youth movements important
- Hitler Pimpfen and Hitler Youth for Boys
- Young Maidens and League of German Maidens for girls
- emphasis on sports and drill/uniforms/marching/camps/discipline
- preparation for warlike activities and unquestioning obedience
- children eventually forced to join youth movements
- recognition that young people were important/had to be trained for the future
- education as indoctrination, eg anti-Semitism; Master Race theories (developed points)

Section B

2. The candidate assesses the completeness of Source A using **presented evidence** such as:

- high unemployment—growing dole queues
- inaction of Weimar politicians
- rise in support for extremist parties (Communism, Nazism)
- desire for dictatorship

History—Credit Level 2000

and **recalled evidence** such as:

- Versailles
- continuation of Reparations until 1932
- dislike of the Constitution/democracy
- inflation of 1923 and 1929
- violence
- appeal of Nazi propaganda
- fear of Communism/Socialism

3. The candidate compares the sources using **evidence** such as:
   - both agree many Germans were discontented:
     Source A = "discontented voters";
     Source B = "discontented German nation"
   - both agree that many Germans blamed Weimar:
     Source A = Weimar politicians have no answers
     Source B = declared themselves against . . . Weimar politicians
   - both agree that many Germans wanted a dictatorship:
     Source A = more and more turn to . . . dictatorship
     Source B = hurrying towards dictatorship
   - both agree that Communists became more popular:
     Source A = rise in support . . . for the Communists
     Source B = The Communists have picked up support
   - both agree that Nazis became more popular:
     Source A = support for the Nazis was spectacular
     Source B = Nazis have made huge gains
   - both agree that Germans turned to Political Parties which opposed Weimar:
     Source A = political parties which opposed Weimar

Source B = Nazis and Communists have picked up support
   - only Source A explains reasons for discontent: high unemployment; dole queues
   - only Source A says that support for Nazism was greater than support for Communism
   - only Source B gives details on scale of Anti-Weimar opinion; "over half of population"

History—Credit Level 2001

Unit I—Context A: 1750s–1850s

Section A

1. The candidate describes the technological changes in cotton production using evidence such as:
   - Kay's flying shuttle
   - Hargreaves' spinning jenny
   - Arkwright's water frame
   - Crompton's mule
   - Cartwright's power loom
   - automated carding machines
   - details on the use /techniques of the above
   - use of water power
   - use of steam power
   - use of mass production techniques

2. The candidate explains whether Scotland's urban housing problems were solved by building tenements using evidence such as:
   - there were not enough houses in urban areas
   - tenements were tall blocks of flats which supplied living space
   - many people could be accommodated in a small space
   - some tenement blocks were well looked after and supplied good conditions
   - some tenements were often built of cheap, inferior materials

History—Credit Level 2001

- overcrowding was often not solved; tenement dwelling was cramped
- tenements were built in close proximity to each other
- facilities often had to be shared
- often-one room dwelling/no bedrooms
- disease was often prevalent
- there was a lack of privacy
- tenements often lacked sanitation or running water
- tenements were sometimes wet and squalid
- some tenants lived in unhygienic basements
- provided accommodation near employment/factories

3. The candidate evaluates Sources A and B using evidence such as:

Source A

- authorship: from reputable historian—likely to be reliable
- limitation: only one author's opinion "Radical war was pathetic"
- content: describes the incident at Bonnymuir
- accuracy: says three Bonnymuir radicals executed: in fact only two resulted from Bonnymuir; otherwise backed up by other evidence

Source B

- authorship: eyewitness/ involved speaker
- contemporaneity: primary source from time of Radical incident
- accuracy: biased account—stating reasons for involvement
- purpose: purpose is to excuse/account for involvement
- content: describes one man's part in events

Both Sources:

Two sides of the argument are given

4. The candidate identifies supporting evidence in the sources such as:

Source A

- events (Bonnymuir) caused alarm among authorities
- newspapers covered the events (Bonnymuir)
- discussions followed events (Bonnymuir)
- later discussions contributed to political change
- "left the authorities looking foolish"

Source B

- James Wilson lost his life for the cause
- Wilson— a pioneering freedom fighter
- Radical activity would help free country from political shame
- Radical events will live in history

Source C

- a number of prisoners taken
- three men were hanged (political martyrs)
- Wilson's hanging was scandalous (aroused sympathy)
- some men were transported (major event)
- juries sympathised with accused men (won public support)

The candidate identifies conflicting evidence in the sources such as:

Source A:

- Radical war was "pathetic"
- Bonnymuir was a "minor skirmish"
- authorities rather foolish at the alarm caused (a lot of fuss about nothing)

Source B

- the authorities are in control
- Radicals were arrested and tried

Source C

- Bonnymuir was just a "short fight"
- only four Radicals were wounded
- only three Radicals executed
- when standard of living improved agitation settled down

History—Credit Level 2001

- newspapers also helped in the fight for political reform (not just Radicals)

5. The candidate offers a conclusion on the issue and shows balance in the answer, using relevant presented evidence as outlined above and recalled evidence such as:

For the issue:

- aim of Bonnymuir was to capture weapons from Carron Iron Works
- Government troops attacked Radicals at Bonnymuir
- John Baird and Andrew Hardie were hanged
- worry about mob riots
- Wilson was involved in a radical march at Strathaven
- 20,000 watched Wilson's death on Glasgow Green
- all three who died became martyrs
- 19 were transported to Australia (the Scottish Insurrectionists)
- newspapers such as "The Scotsman" covered the event
- Bonnymuir brought lack of working class freedoms to public notice

against the issue

- only a small group of Glasgow Radicals marched towards Carron Iron Works
- only 47 prisoners were taken at Bonnymuir
- authorities were alarmed but exaggerated the menace posed
- agents provocateurs exaggerated the events
- military power was always on top of events
- whole Radical War lasted just 5 days
- violence is not a great feature of Scottish working class protest
- other factors played a part in development of democracy

- peaceful protests: petitions; letters to newspapers etc played a part in change
- extension of the franchise came in 1832 (but not to everyone)

Unit I—Context B: 1830s–1930s

Section A

1. The candidate describes changes in coal mining as a result of new technology by 1930 using evidence such as:
   - electrical coal cutting equipment
   - electric lighting
   - safety lighting
   - steam and electrical power to raise cages
   - wagon ways
   - ventilation fans
   - metal or concrete pit pops

2. The candidate explains the reasons why there was so much poor housing during the 19th century using evidence such as:
   - needs of workers to find accommodation
   - high rents/low wages
   - demand outstripped supply
   - many houses badly constructed (jerry built)
   - poor/cheap building materials used
   - housing often not looked after well
   - desire for quick profits
   - needs of industry to house workers/cause of overcrowding
   - population growth/movements and demand for housing
   - lack of central and local government control

Section B

3. The candidate evaluates the sources using evidence such as:

Source A

- authorship: a Suffragette—one converted to their cause
- contemporaneity: speech at a Suffragette function in 1908

History—Credit Level 2001

- content: Suffragettes are getting attention
- accuracy: supporter of the cause so likely bias
- purpose: to win support for Suffragettes: show sympathy for the cause (said at Suffragette function)

Source B

- authorship: written by a modern historian who has researched the topic
- contemporaneity: secondary source with hindsight to events
- content: says government not giving in to law breakers
- limitation: one person's opinion: "law breaking" weakened case

Together, the sources show both sides of the argument

4. The candidate selects evidence that the Suffragettes did harm the "votes for women" cause such as:

Source A

- Suffragettes created rows at Westminster: annoyed MPs: acted against them

Source B

- law breaking strengthened the argument that women could not be trusted/did not deserve the vote
- government took a tough line against Suffragettes
- Suffrage movement split

Source C

- many viewed militancy with disgust
- many believed lawful/peaceful methods were better/more effective

The candidate selects evidence that the Suffragettes did not harm the "vote for women" cause such as:

Source A

- nothing had been done more for the cause
- cause brought to public attention
- more done by Suffragettes than in previous 60 years
- author has been convinced by Suffragette actions

Source B

- Suffragettes believed extreme actions would force the government's hand

Source C

- no attention paid to cause until 1905 when militancy began
- militant tactics have drawn public attention

5. The candidate reaches a balanced conclusion using **presented evidence** such as:

For the issue:

- Government took a tough line against militancy
- people did not trust women
- methods not effective
- suffrage movement divided

Against the issue

- methods brought cause to attention of public and government
- more done by Suffragettes than other groups

and from **recalled evidence** such as:

For the issue:

- details of violence which disgusted people
- anger at Suffragette outrages
- Suffragettes arrested: Government hard line
- Cat and Mouse Act

Against the Issue:

- public sympathy for brave Suffragettes (Hunger Strikers; martyr(s))
- Cat and Mouse Act attracted sympathy
- media attention
- effect of women's war work

History—Credit Level 2001

Unit I —Context C:1880s–Present Day

1. The candidate describes how shipbuilding improved using evidence such as:

   - steam replaced sail
   - turbine engines used
   - diesel engines used
   - bodywork changed from wood to iron then steel
   - ship sections were welded not riveted
   - prefabrication techniques made better ships
   - computer-aided technology used to make ships
   - ship design improved
   - identical ships built to exact specifications
   - electric furnaces used
   - high-tech cranes
   - pneumatic riveters
   - indoor shipbuilding facilities

2. The candidate gives a balanced explanation of whether housing improved in Scotland using evidence such as:

   - council estates built
   - housing moved from city centre to pleasanter outskirts/suburbs
   - high rise flats built: good and bad points
   - prefabs built: good and bad points
   - housing estates could lack community spirit
   - estates experienced vandalism
   - estates often lacked amenities
   - new towns built in 50s and 60s
   - new towns often had good facilities
   - renovation of tenements (1980s)
   - increase in house ownership— houses well looked after
   - great deal of poor housing remained

Section B

3. The candidate evaluates the sources using evidence such as:

   ### Source A
   - authorship: a Suffragette—one converted to their cause
   - contemporaneity: speech at Suffragette function in 1908
   - content: Suffragettes are getting attention
   - accuracy: supporter of the cause so likely bias
   - purpose: to win support for Suffragettes: show sympathy for the cause (said at Suffragette function)

   ### Source B
   - authorship: written by a modern historian who has researched the topic
   - contemporaneity: secondary source with hindsight to events
   - content: says government not giving in to law breakers
   - accuracy: one person's opinion– "law breaking" weakened the case

   Together the sources show both sides of the argument

4. The candidate selects evidence that the Suffragettes did harm the "votes for women" cause such as:

   ### Source A
   - Suffragettes created rows at Westminster; annoyed MPs; acted against them

   ### Source B
   - law breaking strengthened the argument that women could not be trusted/did not deserve the vote
   - government took a tough line against Suffragettes
   - Suffrage movement split

   ### Source C
   - many viewed militancy with disgust
   - many believed peaceful/lawful methods were better/more effective

History—Credit Level 2001

The candidate selects evidence that the Suffragettes did not harm the "vote for women" cause such as:

Source A

- nothing had done more for the cause
- cause brought to public attention
- more done by Suffragettes than in previous 60 years
- author has been convinced by Suffragette action

Source B

- Suffragettes believed extreme actions would force the government's hand

Source C

- no attention paid to cause until 1905 when militancy began
- militant tactics have drawn public attention

5. The candidate reaches a balanced conclusion using **presented evidence** such as:

For the issue:

- Government took a tough line against militancy
- people did not trust women
- methods not effective
- suffrage movement divided

Against the issue

- methods brought cause to attention of public and government
- more done by militant Suffragettes than other groups

and from **recalled evidence** such as:

For the Issue

- details of violence which disgusted people
- anger at Suffragette outrages
- Suffragettes arrested: Government hard line
- Cat and Mouse Act

Against the issue:

- public sympathy for brave Suffragettes (Hunger strikes; martyr(s))
- Cat and Mouse Act attracted sympathy
- media attention
- Suffragettes gave up militancy on outbreak of war
- effect of women's war work

Unit II—Context B: 1890s–1920s

1. (a) The candidate fully assesses the importance of the Alliance System as a cause of World War One using evidence such as:

Rivalries between countries as important causes of tension/ill feeling: eg

- Austria—Hungary v Russia
- Germany v France
- Germany v Britain
- Dual Alliance
- Franco Russian Alliance
- Entente Cordiale
- Triple Alliance
- Terms of the alliances/entente and the possible importance of other factors such as:
    - Pre-war incidents
    - Balkan Wars
    - Militarism
    - Arms race
    - Naval rivalry
    - Nationalism
    - Sarajevo
    - Alliance system in action in 1914

(b) The candidate fully assesses the importance of the Naval Arms Race in causing World War One using evidence such as:

- German Naval Laws
- Naval rivalry/Naval race
- Dreadnoughts
- New naval bases
- Kiel Canal

History—Credit Level 2001

and the possible importance of other factors such as:

- Militarism/build up of armies and weapons
- Army reforms in Europe
- Alliance System
- Rivalries
- Pre-war incidents
- Balkan Wars
- Sarajevo and thereafter

Section B

2. The candidate discusses the attitude of the author towards gas using evidence such as:

   - it is a dreadful weapon
   - it inflicts cruelty
   - it is the tactic of a mass murderer
   - it can win ground
   - it is an object of horror
   - it is a contemptible weapon
   - it is only used by horrible, contemptible armies

3. The candidate evaluates the completeness of the description using **presented evidence** such as:

   - gas causes dreadful results
   - gas is used to try to gain ground
   - gas causes blisters and blinding
   - gas kills by suffocation/choking

   and from **recalled evidence** such as:

   - German use of gas at Ypres in 1915
   - operation of gas canisters/shells
   - types of gas used: mustard; phosgene; tear
   - operation of gas canisters/shells
   - importance of wind direction
   - use of gas masks
   - British use of gas
   - surprise factor of gas
   - effectiveness of gas

Unit II–Context C: 1930s–1960s

Section A

1. The candidate fully assesses the importance of German rearmament in causing World War Two using evidence such as:

   - rearmament broke Treaty of Versailles
   - reintroduction of conscription allowed Hitler to expand size of army quickly
   - naval rearmament could threaten Britain
   - air force essential for Hitler's foreign policy aims
   - France and Britain did nothing to stop rearmament
   - League of Nations powerless to stop rearmament
   - rearmament could threaten countries in East Europe
   - Britain made a naval agreement with Germany in 1935, so accepting Hitler's actions
   - rearmament was only a prelude to Hitler's other foreign policy aims
   - rearmament was a long term cause of war.
   - other immediate causes of war
   - details of how German rearmament increased tension

   The candidate fully assesses the importance of Hitler's actions against Czechoslovakia in causing the second World War using evidence such as:

   - Hitler's demands for Sudetenland—part of Czechoslovakia
   - part of Hitler's aim of a Greater Germany
   - unrest in Sudetenland among German-speaking population (Henlein)
   - Czechoslovakian response (alliances with France and Russia)
   - Chamberlain's meetings with Hitler-Berchtesgaden, Bad Godesberg

History—Credit Level 2001

- British and French attitude–appeasement of Hitler
- Hitler increases demands—crisis deepens
- danger of war close in late September 1938
- Munich Conference called–Hitler gets Sudenteland
- Hitler's assurances of peace in future ("peace in our time")
- weakening of Czechoslovakia-Russian attitude
- Hitler demands rest of Czechslovakia in March 1939
- end of appeasement after extinction of Czechoslovakia
- British and French guarantees in Eastern Europe after March 1939
- war much nearer after failure of appeasement
- way open for aggression v Poland
- possible other causes of war

Section B

2. The candidate evaluates the completeness of Source A using **presented evidence** such as:

   - new Soviet missile sites on Cuba are threatening
   - missiles capable of striking cities in USA
   - missiles aimed at US capital/centre of Government
   - more missile sites being built
   - new missile sites designed to strike cities in the Western hemisphere

   and from **recalled evidence** such as:

   - secret missile sites detected by US spy planes
   - possible Soviet motives were hostile
   - Kennedy announced blockade of Cuba in retaliation
   - Kennedy announced other measures
   - US military build up
   - part of Domino Theory attitude

- US sphere of influence threatened
- US fear and surprise
- threat was of nuclear attack

3. The candidate evaluates the attitude of the author using evidence such as:

   - knows that US wants security
   - wants security for Russia, too
   - says Soviet Union feels surrounded
   - annoyed at US rockets in Turkey
   - says Turkey is closer to Soviet Union than Cuba is to US
   - feels US is being hypocritical
   - all countries wanted/deserved security

Unit III—Context A: USA 1850–1880

Section A

1. The candidate describes problems faced by the native Americans using evidence such as:

   - loss of homeland as boundaries pushed west
   - loss of freedom with removal to reservations
   - destruction of way of life
   - hunting grounds disturbed
   - buffalo destroyed
   - clash of cultures
   - white settlers regarded native Americans as inferior–in need of civilising
   - decline of population: some tribes wiped out
   - diseases (smallpox, measles, cholera) affected tribes
   - alcohol becomes a problem
   - loss of power: tribes not regarded as a nation

2. The candidate explains the reasons for discontent in the South after the Civil War using evidence such as:

   - South defeated
   - Economy in ruins
   - Destruction to land and property
   - Northern troops garrisoned in Southern homes
   - Military rule imposed
   - Freedmen's Bureau

History—Credit Level 2001

- annoyed at rights for ex-slaves
- ex-army personnel unable to vote
- annoyance at carpetbaggers and scallywags
- Blacks still have rights restricted
- Black Codes
- many ex-slaves worse off

Section B

3. The candidate evaluates the source using evidence such as:
    - authorship: published by Republican Party
    - contemporaneity: published at the time of the presidential election
    - purpose: to persuade Americans to vote for Lincoln (propaganda)
    - content: contains information on Lincoln's policies
    - accuracy: propaganda election manifesto poster/biased
    - limitation: only one poster about one (very important) policy

4. The candidate discusses the views in Source B using evidence such as:
    - Union will be split—a line drawn across it
    - War will be waged against slave holding states
    - South will be excluded
    - South will lose equal rights
    - South will lose power of self government
    - Federal Government will become enemy of the South

5. The candidate compares the Sources with reference to features such as:

    Sources disagree about the country being divided:
    - Source A: Lincoln says "the Union shall be preserved"
    - Source B: " a line has been drawn across the Union"

Sources disagree about the preservation of the Union:
- Source A: Lincoln says: "main objective is to save the Union"
- Source B: says "the south shall be excluded".

Sources disagree about national identity:
- Source A shows US flag and the slogan "Rally Round the Flag"
- Source B says the American Government is the enemy of the south.

Sources disagree about slavery:
- Source A says Lincoln's aim is neither to destroy nor save slavery
- Source B says a war will be waged against slavery until it shall cease

Unit III—Context B: India 1917–1947

Section A

1. The candidate describes Indian divisions using evidence such as:
    - religious divisions between Hindus, Muslims, Sikhs etc (often encouraged by British Raj)
    - ethnic divisions—eg between northern Aryans and Southern Dravidians
    - internal differences between princely states and provinces under direct British rule
    - social divisions caused by the Hindu caste system
    - other social divisions caused by economic inequalities
    - political divisions between Congress and Muslim League: often encouraged by British Raj

2. The candidate gives reasons for the popularity of the Congress Party using evidence such as:
    - Congress policy of self-government
    - support for full independence grew from 1929 on
    - Congress aimed to unite all Indians against communalism/ religious divisions (secular party)

History—Credit Level 2001

  – leadership and influence of Gandhi
  – leadership and influence of Nehru
  – various civil disobedience campaigns (examples are possible)
  – gained publicity and support

Section B

3. The candidate evaluates Source A using evidence such as:

  – authorship: British cartoon
  – contemporaneity: at time of Salt March—beginning of civil disobedience campaign
  – accuracy: clearly opposed to Gandhi's tactics
  – limitation: only gives a British view (Civil Disobedience is a monster)
  – purpose: to criticise/discredit Gandhi's tactics
  – content: refers to civil disobedience tactics

4. The candidate compares the sources using evidence such as:

Sources agree that Gandhi supported civil disobedience:

  – Source A shows Gandhi summoning the genie of civil disobedience
  – Source B states Ghandi's intention to use civil disobedience

Sources disagree about how civil disobedience will be controlled

  – Source A suggests that civil disobedience will get out of control (Gandhi will not be able to control it
  – Source B says civil disobedience will be "organised" and "peaceful"

Sources disagree about the nature of civil disobedience:

  – Source A suggests that civil disobedience will lead to violence; menacing figure of the genie and "disobedient words"

  – Source B says that civil disobedience is not intended to hurt anyone

Sources disagree about British view of civil disobedience:

  – Source A shows a hostile British view
  – Source B says the tactics will work to convert the British/ check organised violence of government

Only Source B says that the tactics are in response to British violence

Only Source B gives reasons for the campaign

5. The candidate evaluates the attitudes shown in Source B using evidence such as:

  – does not want to harm any British
  – thinks British rule is a curse (bad for India)
  – thinks only non-violence can combat British violence
  – wants to show British people that British rule is wrong
  – plans to combat the salt tax through civil disobedience
  – feels he has no alternative to civil disobedience

Unit III—Context C: Russia 1914–1941

Section A

1. The candidate describes the hardships faced by Russian peasants using evidence such as:

  – high taxes
  – farms too small to feed a family
  – old fashioned farming methods
  – very little machinery
  – redemption debts had to be paid
  – poor housing
  – poor standard of living
  – frequent food shortages/famine
  – restricted freedom
  – further effects of the war
  – did not own land
  – oppressed by secret police
  – harsh climate
  – treatment of kulaks

History—Credit Level 2001

2. The candidate explains why Lenin thought the time was right for revolution using evidence such as:

   - Provisional Government was unpopular
   - growing anarchy in the country
   - unrest in towns: food and fuel shortages
   - people tired of war
   - Bolsheviks promised to end the war
   - Provisional Government lost support of army
   - growing support for Bolshevik ideas
   - Bolsheviks won support through role in Kornilov Revolt
   - Red Guards now armed
   - Bolshevik slogans: Peace Bread and Land
   - Bolsheviks had gained control of Petrograd and Moscow Soviets
   - Lenin's self-belief: "Go now; Do not wait."

Section B

3. The candidate identifies the attitude of Stalin using **presented evidence** such as:

   - strongly supports agricultural change in Russia
   - believes small farms must be joined into larger farms
   - argues that workers must cooperate on larger farms
   - insists changes should take place gradually
   - believes peasants should be persuaded not forced
   - insists that this is the only solution to agricultural problems

4. The candidate evaluates Source B using evidence such as:

   - authorship: official government photographer
   - contemporaneity: primary source from the period of collectivisation
   - content: shows party workers talking to peasants (farm workers)
   - accuracy: government propaganda
   - purpose: aimed at persuading peasants to carry out collectivisation
   - limitation: only shows what happened in one part of Russia/ on one occasion

5. The candidate compares the sources using evidence such as:

   Sources agree that party officials went out to encourage collectivisation:

   - Source B shows people listening to a party official
   - Source C says party men sent out

   Sources agree that persuasion was used:

   - Source B shows a peaceful discussion/lecture
   - Source C talks about encouraging peasants

   Sources disagree about methods used:

   - Source B—peaceful persuasion
   - Source C—threats/violence

   Only Source B shows propaganda posters being used

   Only Source C mentions use of security men and violence

Unit III—Context D: Germany 1918–1939

Section A

1. The candidate describes the reasons for German anger over Versailles using evidence such as:

   - not based on Wilson's 14 points
   - a dictated peace
   - War Guilt Clause
   - huge reparations
   - loss of territory in Europe (examples accepted as one developed point)
   - loss of colonies
   - military restrictions/disarmament
   - ban on Anschluss
   - German perceived threat of invasion

History—Credit Level 2001

2. The candidate gives reasons for Nazi support between 1933 and 1939 using evidence such as:

   - fear of SS/Brownshirts
   - fear of concentration camps
   - appeal of Nazi policies
   - employment increased/unemployment decreased
   - lack of effective opposition
   - Hitler's abilities as an orator
   - Nazi propaganda including radio and cinema
   - rallies and parades
   - Youth activities
   - provided strong leadership
   - appeared to solve economic problems
   - only one legal political party
   - strict control/totalitarian state
   - control of education

3. The candidate evaluates Source A in terms of evidence such as:

   - authorship: photograph and should be reliable?
   - contemporaneity: primary source from Nazi era
   - accuracy: matches other evidence on treatment of Jewish children (textbooks)
   - content: shows children being humiliated in class
   - purpose: anti-Semitic propaganda
   - limitation: only one classroom in one part of Germany

4. The candidate compares the sources using evidence such as:

   Both Sources agree that Jewish children were humiliated:

   - Source A shows children being shamed
   - Source B says Jewish girl arrived at home after being humiliated

   Both sources agree that Jewish children were separated in class:

   - Source A shows two Jewish children at the blackboard
   - Source B says the teacher separated Aryan and non Aryan children

   Both sources agree that the Jewish children were made an example of:

   - Source A shows them standing in front of the blackboard
   - Source B says that the teacher told the Aryans to study the non Aryans for signs of Jewishness

   Both Sources highlight the role teacher played in the humiliation of the Jews:

   - Source A teacher supervising the humiliation of the Jews.
   - Source B says that the teacher organised the humiliation of the Jews

   Both Sources agree that Jews were treated as enemies:

   - Source A: blackboard slogan says "Jews are our greatest enemies".
   - Source B: Aryan and Jewish children were now enemies.

5. The candidate discusses the attitudes conveyed in the Source, using evidence such as:

   - says that Christians in Munich are against the violence
   - says much sympathy and compassion is shown towards Jews
   - says some Aryans are willing to shelter Jews
   - thinks the ban on Jews using shops is harsh
   - says grocers ignored the ban (were sympathetic to Jews)
   - says bakers ignored the ban and sold to Jews (sympathetic to Jews)
   - Christians generally in favour of Jews

Leckie & Leckie has made every effort to trace all copyright holders. If any have been inadvertently missed, Leckie & Leckie will be pleased to make the necessary arrangements. Leckie & Leckie would like to thank the following for their permission to use their material: Wiener Library (Holocaust, Third Reich) for the photograph on page 142.